'Savitz marches through time with an intention that forges meaning and questions the stories we tell ourselves while gently erasing our indescribable inclination to define. She moves like a thoughtful flaneur on a hunt for significance while relaying her trials and tribulations in such a deeply personal manner that they somehow come to feel like your own. She generously invites you into her esoteric ring while articulating which universally personal fables we hold onto and those we leave behind. Through her own experiences she observes that life is endlessly rich, complicity is dangerous, and being honest with ourselves is the answer to everything.'
~ Sonya Naumann, Photographer,
professor of photography

'Fish Eyes For Pearl's is an extraordinary experience of a wondrous journey with a daring host, Masha Savitz, serving up life and death in gift wrapped prose, poetry romance, rock and roll, cinema, and inspiration for all'
~ Jeff 'the Dude' Dowd the holy fool Jeff bridge played In the Big Lebowski.

'In her delicate but powerfully woven first novel, Masha Savitz, with style and courage, delineates the threads that bind us all, both temporally and physically, across time and space. It is at once a damning indictment of preconceived notions, a dedication to sacrifice, and the palpable scars of our hidden collective wounds. Both lyrical and brutal, Fish Eyes for Pearls confronts us with the capricious whimsy, the irony and the tragedy of our shared and savage existential dilemmas.'
~ Pete McGrain. Writer/filmmaker

'This novel is an intellectually and emotionally stimulating journey of the soul. Savitz's writing harkens back to the great writers of the 20th century, with the same beauty as Rilke and similar metaphysical sensibility of Jorge Luis Borges. She infuses in her work, a beautiful sensuality, and a sincere, vulnerable eroticism that goes beyond sexuality into a place of spiritual concepts. This is a novel of a higher order; it is a masterpiece and deserves praise. Savitz stands alone and has reached new heights changing the landscape of literature.'
~ Adam Michardi, filmmaker

'Savitz is a genius study of discovery, bravely trudging forward with the age old stoic backing of the knowledge of being an intelligent female creator in a world that was drawn by men.'
~ Tanna Frederick, Actress

To Abba, my father, Herman Savitz, lover of books, teller of tales, embodiment of faith and compassion.

My sixth grade English Teacher,
Geraldine Jackson

And to all my muses, and those who whilst gently holding onto the gold cord, as ocean pearls are procured and polished, help me deliver the moon back into the night sky.

FISH EYES FOR PEARLS

MASHA SAVITZ

This a work is magical realism memoir. The events, people, and places are factual, though names and descriptions may be altered to protect anonymity. All depictions are based on my interpretation, reflecting my perceptions, aesthetics, and sensibilities, literary and otherwise.

Edited by Pete McGrain

Library of Congress Control Number: 2018938569
Names: Savitz, Masha.
Title: Fish eyes for pearls / Masha Savitz.
Description: Venice, CA : O'Shan Press, [2018]
Identifiers: ISBN 9780692898253
Subjects: LCSH: Savitz, Masha. | Screenwriters--Biography. | Magic realism (Literature) | LCGFT: Creative nonfiction. | Autobiographies.
Classification: LCC PS3619.A88 Z46 2018 | DDC 813/.6--dc23

O'Shan Press

O'SHAN PRESS

'An invisible red thread connects those who are destined to meet regardless of time, place or circumstance. The thread may stretch or tangle but will never break.'
~ A Chinese Proverb

'Archangel Cassiel watches the events of the cosmos unfold with little interference. He is the angel of solitude and tears and is said to preside over the moon, karma and time.'
~ Author unknown

"In the muddy human world, pearls and fish eyes are jumbled together."
~ Li Hongzhi

I plot my escape from the crib.

This earliest memory is colored pewter, pussy willow bud fuzz and powdery blue.

I hear the breeze suck in the window shade that feigns dusk, then exhaling, reveals in outline, the unmistakable incandescent glow of summer afternoon.

I don't want to nap any more
I want to go to the park.

But, everyone is asleep this Saturday.

The wooden chair that my mother has painted glossy turquoise at the end of my crib should suffice, my accomplice, accessory, and liberation participation invitation.

I straddle one foot over the bar, leveraging my body across the top bar. Oooeeee!, Painful between my little legs as I hoist myself-

over

the

edge.

One foot onto the chair, now just a hop-slide down onto solid floor from here.

Eyeing my younger sister, still asleep in her crib across the room that we share, I glide out the door, a stealth provocateur.

Now to wake up my father who promises to take me to the park after naps.

I'm free!

Sort of.

) ((●)) (

All of the belongings of an elderly woman in my first Boston apartment, who has just died, are heaped onto the Commonwealth Avenue curbside; a lifetime scattered on pavement.

Rushing to catch the trolley, or T, to my morning painting class, I pause and pay homage to this life I never encountered. Her possessions, the compilation of a life lived, considered, grieved, cherished, reconciled and savored, are now strewn for the picking. So I do.

Rummaging through her things, I discover a formal wedding party photo with a somber groom in a WW ll uniform that will become a large painting with a disturbing sense of military, matrimony and memory, depicted in rose and steel grays. I slip the black and white mat photo into to my bag.

I also salvage a small, carnation pink, leather address book- its lines unmarked. This little book, pages yellowing and brittle, the frayed binding now secured with packing tape, is filled with the significant names of my life, and each time used, recalls the women I never met and the single pink thread that stitches the stories of my life to her hers, and now, to all the others.

My jubilee birthday quickly approaching, I recall and compile these stories, the contents of my life.

As such, I am lead on a mission to gather and liberate ghosts with an ever growing awareness that we are all connected. I navigate the thorny and humbling landscape of relationships, society, and the unseen realms, all processed through varied creative undertakings, on canvas, with words, and as viewed through a camera lens, turning life into art, and art into a life.

These stories are spun like a web, honoring a chronology of impressions, designs and pattern in circular and spiraling fashion, to the rhythm of a meteorite shower.

I flicker in and out of the space like a swimmer in butterfly stroke, in and out of being caterpillar and butterfly, in and out of time and space, like these stories.

Some moments I am drawn into another realm, where past memories of love and sorrow, lessons and yearnings, with golden dust-like strands, forge the place where this book lives and is being written.

Perhaps, it's the same place where the phrase 'fisheyes and pearls' is coined, in an ancient book of internal alchemy. It prompts me to ask, in this world veiled in illusion, how do we discern the precious from the common or worthless? And, then, how might we transform the ordinary into something extraordinary?

CHAPTER ONE

six degrees

There are different cafés for different moods and tasks depending on the time of light. This is especially important during New England winters when pure sunlight is at a premium and little should be squandered in a dark atmospheric establishment. It is also a meager defense against the melancholia that comes with the first autumnal frost that lingers until a window can be safely cracked open on occasional April nights.

I had well observed at what time of year the sun would stream into the large south side windows in the airy Carberries Cafe on Prospect Street, or filter in down the stairs of the European French Patisserie in Harvard Square. The window tables at the Trident Cafe on Newbury Street maximize indirect light offer ideal people watching, concurrently.

Similarly, there are copious cafe options to choose from in Berkeley.

Soon, however, there will be one cafe that will become home base, the center of all social life, and in some cases antisocial life, theatrical stage, school, production company, soirée, editing bay, salon, existential prison, a microcosmic mirror.

But not yet.

Even the perfume I wear is a cafe-

Cafe Rose

Top notes: saffron, black pepper and may rose.

Middle notes: turkish rose, Bulgarian rose and coffee.

Base notes: Incense, amber, sandalwood and patchouli.

) ((●)) (

Having not painted since the Berkeley move, I don't know how to re-enter my work.

Start at the beginning, I deduce, return to my first painting crush, my first artist love with whom I feel akin- French post impressionist painter-Pierre Bonnard.

At Moe's Book on Telegraph I scan the Bonnard collection downstairs, pouring over the pages as I had done in art school.

The borrowed library book, always propped up against the foot of my easel, open to a color print that never came close to capturing the luminosity of the original, now splattered with turpentine drips in Bonnard hues. One of his still-lives could beckon me, with its shimmering color, from across a museum. And it has.

I pen poems.

Flesh rainbow,
an arching back
across canvas like an opalescent
bridge, connecting corporal form
with the inner-envisioned world
of ideas and spirit.
Patterns and jutting edges,
ambiguous red
and vulva pink angle,
pushing up through the corner,
tightly arranged
like sitar strings,
A series of verticals,
vibrating with color.
A bent knee, a foot

extended in a marine like haze
where the contours of a
Woman emerges
From this deep
Prussian
blue.

leaning figure
balanced on two violet
legs, vanishes to a point
where female figure poses
beside a porcelain tub –
brown
in the shape
of dog
against white.

Images,
hues like abalone shell
reveal the shimmering
interiors of intimacies,
a life.

This is the life I admire and desire, identifying with Bonnard's aesthetics evident by his choice of subject matter- Marthe, his lover, in the bath, dressing at an open window, or sitting amidst a bowl of ripe fruit.

His love of the intimate lives in me too and I yearn for the relationship they seem to share, bonded by these

moments, forever captured in radiant pigment.
A realization, would soon however, challenge my perception, change my course. It would pass so quietly, yet would shake foundations.

) ((●)) (

As I bend and twist at the edge of my bed, buckling my suede ankle boots, the worn post card of a Bonnard print hanging across the room above the light switch by the door, catches my eye.

A revolution ensues.

Everything has to be reconfigured. My usual cafe will not do - too many distractions.

At La Batou Evre, with it's salmon pink linens and classical music wafting, a cafe where I am anonymous, a story will be conceived, gestate and birthed.

) ((●)) (

Sculpting with words, at the La Batou Evre, I craft a story.

Marthe and Pierre

Marthe, the model and later wife of the French painter, Pierre Bonnard, was a sensitive woman. Easily offended by the vulgarity and harshness of Parisians and most people in general, she withdrew from social life. As a defense against this predisposition, she created a beautiful world in which only she and her husband lived. In fact it was such a place of refinement and simple profound charm that Pierre surrendered willingly to her insistence that he remain home with her. He was happily seduced into her magical universe, content to render and record its moments and subtle movements.

Occasionally he would sneak out to the café, the dog as a pretext, hoping to meet Matisse or some other friends. The other painters were not altogether understanding of his allegiance to Marthe and the severe restrictions on his freedom. Many gossiped that she was 'unbalanced.' To an artist, balance and beauty are synonymous and certainly, Pierre, a Libra, knew balance, and Marthe knew beauty – she lived in it and he lived for it. Their life together was like a brilliant gem, created and held in a masterfully designed ring, set upon a finger, perfectly contained unto itself.
Their home, the center of their life and backdrop to all events, was a cathedral of light. The dining

room table was an altar, complete with goblets, wine and sacrificial flowers. The bath was Marthe's sanctuary. With steam rising like incense, she submerged herself in warm baptismal waters, and meditation. This is where she found solace.

Pierre's painting was his favored form of prayer- an extension of his own soul- stirrings and yearnings. So, like a devout parishioner, he portrayed her in devotion, ritually robing, anointing herself with fragrant oil, or setting the fruit offering on the table by the open window.

He not only succeeded in capturing the quality of light around them, but as he created, Pierre had the wondrous ability to add to it. He was known to mutter as he worked- 'It's still color, it is not yet light.'

In fact, there was so much luminosity in this place that even angels were attracted to linger. And they did.

It happened at this time that I too was living in the world of spirits. It was late summer, when the air is heavy with the scent of tuberose, honeysuckle and jasmine and the garden is saturated with lustrous color, boasting fucias, violets, oranges, buttery yellow, purbleberry and red.

Together they had morning coffee, only the

sound of birds could be heard.

Marthe would perform the daily bathing rites, a ceremony that could take hours, as Pierre followed with easel and pallet to worship by her side. He set up his new canvas which he had prepared the night before.

This new painting seemed to compose itself with remarkable ease. Each color mixed, resonated, shimmered and glowed like fiery embers as each stroke was gently laid against the other, seemingly effortless, yet executed with exacting intention.

In spontaneous celebration of the day's triumphant accomplishment, Pierre took his wife passionately in his arms and danced her to the feather bed in the next room. Tenderly, they made love in a rare moment of demonstrative affection and openness between them.

The intensity of light was so great that late summer afternoon that I was somehow drawn down into their lives. There, for a brief moment, a beautiful few weeks, I was their union, their celestial collaboration, delicate tendrils of DNA creation. Their child.

But, like the cut wild flowers on the nightstand, it wasn't to last. It was revealed to me, shortly thereafter, that this was not my time to incarnate into human form- I was called back to the other side.

I was deeply sad to leave Marthe. Although I had to abandon her corporeal body, I remained hovering near by as long as I could.

Is it possible that the lost pregnancy only aggravated Marthe's already sensitive nature, propelling her to retreat further into herself and into the rituals which comforted, soothed and sustained her?

Perhaps too, Pierre's seclusion was in part feeling responsible for her sorrow, or his own unexpressed grief and loss which kept him devoted. Perhaps he needed to connect to her and her pain in order to feel his.

Sadly however, portraying his companion in those intimate scenes and exposed manner, was the only way he knew to express his own vulnerability. Maybe it was really himself floating in the bathtub, expressionless, submerged in amber speckled indigo paint.

Pierre accepted that this was closeness. A canvas always between them, keeping him emotionally exiled from the woman he yearned to know and, in some intrinsic way, from himself.

So, despite all of Marthe's efforts to avoid loneliness and isolation, she remained painfully alone, her partner never able to enter her world, only able to describe it in radiant detail.

That which we most want is what we push away, and that which we are most determined to keep at bay, we invite in.

They never spoke about the miscarriage, but I believe they both sensed my presence. I recognized myself in Pierre's work as if he had depicted my very essence. Sometimes I appear as a vibrant violet surrounding Marthe like an aura. Other times I am the golden green ochre atmosphere in Pierre's self portraits. I was delighted to be recorded in their lives.

Decades later, I was offered the opportunity to take earthly form. Yet, so strong were my impressions and memory of Pierre and Marthe that I awoke driven to construct a life of poetic duality, cherishing the simple pleasures, while finding the sacred in the mundane, the holy in the profane, and elevate it all.

The curious revelation, sitting at the edge of my Berkeley bed, buckleing my boots, was the sudden response to my direct view of a Bonnard's print above the light switch- it was never Pierre's aesthetic or sensual sensibilities that I had shared. But, rather those of Marthe! It was Marthe all along.

How had I not see this before!

I would still however, need to learn something it seemed they had not- to merge while maintaining self, supple, yet solid, able to oscillate in and out of forms, expressing in multiple modes. To sing, harmonizing with the choir, or solo center stage in a scarlet chiffon gown with a symphony, or acapella, or dressed in a black tailed suit, the conductor - blending the extremes of piccolo, flute and oboe to bass clarinet, bassoon and tuba in a glorious monsoon of sound.

) ((●)) (

After college I take extra work as an artist's model. Being both artist and model, I am highly attentive to what would yield suitable compositions from every angle, how impeccably still I must sit to compensate for the students' inexperience. So, I become like marble for the burgeoning talent.

At the Boston art school, I slip out of the silk robe and take my place on the gray model stand. While in a long pose, I amuse myself with the thought that the more empty I am, the more affective I am. Ideas, emotions, ambitions, irrelevant and cumbersome. Less is more. I am potent in non-action, non-thought, not doing. Still-ness. Still-life.

This will be my modus operandi, proving efficacious in many arenas.

Soon I will receive a copy of the Tao de Ching, as I attempt to scale the scaly relationship between artist and model, Pierre and Marthe, man and woman. Because scales are smooth or rough depending on the direction the surface is stroked.

Marthe and others, will each become salmon pink threads woven into this tapestry. Principal of yielding yin.

) ((●)) (

As I write about the Bonnard's, the picture of their relationship fans out before me. I cringe with embarrassment as if I have eavesdropped on a private moment, a door slightly ajar.

Maybe these insights are real, or, perhaps, just the machinations of imagination.

And would it matter?
Such is the dynamic between fact and fiction. The metaphor, the story, is the essential, like Jacob's ladder. Make believe. Believe and make. The intersection of art and life.

Some artists live at these coordinates, others just shop on the corner.

Henry lives at the intersection.
I watch my first Henry Jaglom film, *Someone To Love,* at the Nickelodeon. One of my friends works here, so I feast on art house films. This film lingers in my mind long after I leave the theater, along with the name 'Jaglom.'

I will come across his name years later and will actually meet and get to know this creative maverick, witnessing the intricate personal and professional relationship between he and Tanna, another male and female creative duet.

Interviewing Henry is like being in one of his movies. Even the cafe and table we are sitting at will appear in his films. Lines blur.

Interview with Henry Jaglom and Tanna Frederick
The filmmaker and his Muse

Epoch Times News Paper By Masha Savitz.
LOS ANGELES—The subjects of creativity and show biz

are certainly matters about which Henry Jaglom can claim expertise, as he has worked as an actor, writer, editor and director. And after decades in the business the pioneering indie filmmaker has known and worked with legends, including Orson Wells, Jack Nicholson, Greta Scacchi, Dennis Hopper, and Vanessa Redgrave.

I met Tanna and Henry at their usual haunt in Santa Monica, California, joined by Ron Vignone, the film's award-winning editor, who also plays Gio in Queen of the Lot.

We discussed the genesis of expression, with Talmudic intonation, and the paradoxical nature of some actors who feel most themselves or authentic when playing another character, and whether this is, therefore, their true authentic nature (very Talmudic).

Tanna, revealing a tender vulnerability, explained that she identified with her character Maggie, who says, 'It's not the Hollywood hype that scares me, it's being in the kitchen and eating dinner that scares me. It's the little things.'

The moments of her life that she recalls most vividly are the ones in which she is performing, reflects Tanna. The times she spent by herself she describes as feeling naked.

'The people I know feel more authentic on stage or in a role. They give themselves permission to express themselves through another medium... They know that character better than they know themselves,' explains Tanna, addressing the matter of actors always being 'on.'

'I feel like I'm floating in a strange void when I have no character to latch on to. I feel very uncomfortable with who I am.' Says the woman who, movie website New York Movie Guru lauds as a 'sexy, charismatic, and immensely talented actress.'

Nonetheless, Tanna wonders if she might not suffer from 'a defective personality trait.'

Redirecting the subject, she describes Henry as 'a puppy trying to stay warm, like puppies through a store window. His films are like a whole bunch of people trying to stay warm emotionally, through words.'

Henry, touched by the analogy, acknowledged that films were a way to create a home in a world where he didn't quite feel he belonged.

'Home is what my movies were to me—finding home in my mind, imagination, and dreams.'

'I'm allowed fiction now. It doesn't all have to be autobiographical because I satisfied the other thing, (not having a sense of home) I have this in real life. I don't need to create a home,' Henry says of personal journaling and of his films as he points to Tanna across the table.

'I wanted endless traces of myself—it was the only way I could understand life.' Recounts Henry of his need to write in order to feel or ensure his existence. 'I only stopped keeping a journal when I met you,' he says to Tanna, 'I feel

seen—I feel seen and known.'
'Now I'm looking outward,' asserts Henry, adding that his most recent projects reflect 'what I have learned and seen around me. I have a great vehicle to express it—Tanna.'

When I inquired about what contributed to his evolution into the comic realm, he surmised, 'A reflection of my being happy.'

Henry and Tanna. Pierre and Marthe.

My life informs my art, which informs my life in an ongoing conversation, leading me to examine my own biological parents and 'this' life.

) ((●)) (

Renee and Herman.
Artist and Rabbi.
With the same heat sensitive lens that I viewed the Bonnards, I turn my gaze upon my blood parents. What is it to be the product of a rabbi and an artist?

Like Herman Hesse's, Narcissus and Goldmund, my parents are the next puzzle pieces to understanding myself.
I peek, peer into the obvious and come close to the

mysteries. Sometimes I peer into the mysteries and come close to the obvious.

) ((●)) (

I scrawl in the bathtub:

In this life, I must synthesize the fragmented existence of oppositions - love and freedom

Reconciling desire and disappointment, creating, not just a painting, but a life- colorful, sublime, complex, balancing and transmuting tensions from the chaos, from the yearning- into light.'

'It's still color, says Pierre, 'it is not yet light.'

As the water pours a steady stream from the faucet, I soak and float in the amniotic waters of my claw foot bath- sea salts and oils in musky, woodsy and floral fragrances by my side, remembering and reinventing my life.

) ((●)) (

I had left all of my paintings, the series of Urns, Genesis Women, and many more, in the Boston studio-freedom always exacts a price.

It is a big warehouse, once a recording studio, at the end of the Red line that I rent with art school crony, Molly, a statuesque red head who wears turquoise and olive to offset her hair, but only once my ex has moved out.

'I wouldn't get a studio if I was you,' he warns, 'you can't afford this.'
His way of keeping my feet bound, china cup small.

I knock down walls and rebuild, my way of defying immobilized teacup feet, with the guidance of Tania who works at New Words Bookstore in Central Square and is handy with power tools.

I parlay a green velvet couch from the antique store on the ground floor and Molly contributes a mini-fridge and hot plate from our college dorm days.

The gloaming gray skyline from the huge wall of studio windows washes me in despair- intense longing, utter loneliness, yet a certain comfort, a strange joy mingles with this emptiness.

Maybe this is Hope, or just the compensatory satisfaction that comes with truthful freedom.

Minstrel, mystery, mysteria,
Wisteria- climbing woody vines
Purple and white flowers
Wistful.
Winsome. Loose some.

The Portuguese have a word for this 'saudade,' sadhappy.

Always wistful. In a perpetual state of longing for something in the future that reminds me of something in my past- or someone else's.

We throw memorable parties at the loft studio. I still have photos somewhere. My champagne colored dress, champagne, and the green couch, smiles. Yet this smile, unlike so many other photo smiles, is real, because I know my life with W is done.

Molly has won a Fulbright to study in Ireland. I will set out to get full of bright, and sit in an Irish bar draped in plush curtains pretending to be in the Celtic isle itself.

) ((●)) (

Some days I have the studio all to myself.

I blast the music, sing along, loud:

Companion to our demons, they will dance, and we will play

With chairs, candles, and cloth making darkness in the day.

The picture needs to be unified. I mix paint with mostly terps that I dab on the top of the canvas, streaks rain down in translucent color

It will be easy to look in or out upstream or down without a thought and if I shed a tear I won't cage it.

I stand back. Evaluate.

I won't fear love
and if I feel a rage I won't deny it.
I won't fear love.'

Sarah Mclachlan's song is known to leave me on the studio floor in a state.

Music makes significant contributions to regulating emotions, pacing for maximum potency and delivery.

Sometimes I dance around the easel with brushes in hand, praying that I might paint like this singer who composes with sounds of bells and birds, breaking glass and genres, anything for texture and emotion, bold, tender, fertile.

'And how we'd wished to live in the sensual world
You don't need words--just one kiss, then another.' ~ ~ Kate Bush

I might stand intently in front of the large beveled edge mirror balancing against the studio wall. Face contorting, eyes squinting to simplify forms by distinguishing shadow from light. I study myself, shifting weight and twisting torso. My gaze sharpens, forms swell creating shapes via their contradiction of beautiful negative shape.

This day, I cross the room and collapse into the stained ochre armchair with faded floral print, positioned in full view of the self-portraits. These images are rendered in a myriad of gestures- nude, in black bra and trousers, antique slips, or donning a dragon print robe loosely draped over shoulders exposing a pale breast.

Particular about what I wear even at age three, I insist on white lace tights- North Eastern freezing temperatures don't dissuade. I'm a warrior for my aesthetic, undeterred by pleading parents, seasons or fashion.

When I am four, a pair of ruffled baby bloomers embellished with lace on the backside, feels painfully tight at the elastic. I try to deny this metamorphosis, but it appears that I am growing, growing right out of them.

Horrible. I am crushed by this inevitability. I wish so

hard to halt the mushrooming, so that this favored garment will still fit, but I can't arrest such a persistent process.

I lose the battle to this force, but I will later discover that grown-ups also have many options for lacy silky under things. This will serve as a fine reason to grow up, along with getting to stay up as late as I want, wearing white go-go boots and irony.

And sometimes my childhood wishes *do* come true. When I look out into the world, my seven year old perception sees Marlene Davis, a curvy mom of four in my suburban NJ town in my periphery, shepherding her small flock.

'Nope', I think, 'I never want to grow up to be this.'

I learn that some wishes made with a child's purity and fervor can indeed come true. I never grow up to be 'that.' I don't have children or a house, a mate, or even a carrot peeler. I do have an easel, gold leaf sheets and Kings Blue oil paint. Sometimes I wish my wish was not quite as efficacious and thorough. *Some* of 'that' might have been nice.

) ((●)) (

My work fills the studio wall. There are pencil sketches, ink drawings, some composed on the pages of a discarded encyclopedia, volume 'J', found on the curb in a blue recycle bin. Among the obsessive collection are energetic acrylic finger paintings made on the studio floor as well as large oil paintings on canvas, a symphony of layered pallet knife strokes arranged like jeweled mosaics.

Hypnotized, I stare at the deluge of self portraits, that resemble myself in varying degrees. Thoughts wander. I fidget with a kneaded eraser while contemplating coffee, sunken deep in the worn cushions and wooden arms of this found and cherished chair.

The faces on the wall stare back at me. One peeks behind an easel, another figure strikes a confident pose, others take humble squatting positions.

So many occasions I have removed clothes and stood naked hoping to uncover something, a truth, my essence.

Surveying my body in detail, witnessing and recording like a topographer, endeavoring discovery.

I wait like a true disciple, believing that a cryptic message like a biblical verse would be revealed, the meaning of my existence, my purpose, a sagacious aspect not yet seen.

Cleaving to my reflection, as if peering into a placid lake, ready to dive and merge with the refection, submerge, then emerge as one, like an infant who experiences herself in a mirror for the first time, I am enticed, intrigued, engaged but ultimately disappointed by the impenetrable unyielding surface- the canvas itself.
I am an artist struggling with the limitations and contradictions of creating depth on a flat plain, an illusion of space.

I lay down paint and scratch into the textured work, digging in with the thin wooden end of my brush.

How deep can I go, determined to invoke revelation? I am model and painter, Pierre and Marthe, victim and voyeur, captive and captivated, driven to express my own subjective existence through a preoccupation with 'objective', calculating observation.

The petulance of youth!

It has been my intention all along to go back and retrieve my paintings from the studio once settled in the Bay Area. However, the building was sold six months later and I lost all of my work.

The phase of life called 'letting go' is lasting longer

than anticipated.

'One day this will all reverse.' I think, easing the grief of my tenacious Cancerian self. But I am very wrong, it would never reverse. The relationship of creating or having, is entirely contingent on my ability or willingness to let go- emptiness and nothingness, of which I seem to have in spades. Blades.

My second year in art school, I meet on the trolley car, one of the more talented students who has just graduated. I am eager to hear her great adventures beyond the school walls, her experiences out in the world as a painter.

'I don't paint much, I'm working as an undercover shopper at Sacs Fifth Ave.' She reports.

I nod smiling, "That's cool".
That is *not* cool

Note to self: 'Don't do this.'

I am determined that following graduation, I will not fall into this trap. I must continue to paint and construct my own structure.

Upon getting my degree, I move into a painting studio in East Boston, requiring of myself twenty to forty painting hours per week, calculating this to equal a part time job. I keep a log, hire a model, schedule drawing nights where other artists come to sketch.

I never need to log hours after this. I successfully internalize this rhythm that becomes as natural and consistent as bathing. I approach all creative endeavors as a job, guarding and respecting this time as a work commitment, it serves me well through painting, writing, and filmmaking and living an artful existence.

You see, I'm only half talented. Talented enough to not give up, not talented enough for it ever to be easy. So, self discipline is a most crucial attribute.

Aglaope, called, Agi, a girl with the name of a Siren, who perhaps bares the same fate and function as the beings who lure sailors to their death with their irresistible voices, is one of my hired models. She is a Taurus with long brown hair and soft round features, and her obsession with small animals makes me wonder why she identifies with vulnerability.

After Agi rejects the blonde sales clerk at the bookstore cafe with blue eyes and pointy features, he takes his own life by jumping off a building, only after buying her a most extraordinary exotic flower arrangement. She becomes my roommate.

Franz Kafka in 1917, the same year Bonnard meets Renee, writes, 'Now the Sirens have a still more fatal weapon than their song, namely their silence. And though admittedly such a thing never happened, it is still conceivable that someone might possibly have escaped from their singing; but from their silence certainly never.' Agi is rather silent about many things.

Looking at loft space in downtown Boston, I am introduced to a couple, filmmakers with their baby girl Anushka, full of grace, in tow, asleep in her stroller.

In this abandon warehouse space I find a Super 8mm camera left behind on a door knob in its worn black leather case. I take it home and keep it for years without having an inkling of what to do with it.

Anushka will grow up to be a character in my first screenplay, "Weight of Light".

After bringing the camera to each new home and city, I finally pass it on to a young film student who shares an

office in the same building as me in Venice.
I too will become a filmmaker, but not until I give the camera away. Such is the principal of loss and gain.

Irony from certain angles is lyrical, and from others, just cruel.

) ((●)) (

Cambridge, where I often imagine E.E. Cummings walking down cobblestone streets in chilly moon lit nights, is where my neighbor Liza, married to a beautiful Frenchman, Stephan, who plays the accordion, lives in the adjacent building. The interior of their home is painted red and resounds with laughter, table banging and singing at dinner parties where red wine amply flows.

Liza wears Femme du Boi and speaks perfect French.

I buy myself a bottle too, but am never good at French.

je t'aime mon chéri
je t'aime je t'aime

Stephan will gift me a pen and ink drawing of symbols of the sea, like elegant ancient calligraphy from a Lumarian court in the Indian and Pacific ocean, an aquatic language of his own making, a cherished piece of art.

Our apartments are connected by fire escapes in the rear of the building. I don't consider it as a fire escape, but rather a fetching balcony.
I badly want a porch to perch and write, but really what I need is an escape.

Femm du Boi

Top notes : orlynge blossom, Turkish rose, honey and beeswax

Heart notes: violet, plum, peach, cardamom and cinnamon

Base notes: clove, vanilla and musk.

The languid bottle is the color of dried rose petals.

The fragrance will be recreated years later by designer Serge Lutens, now called Feminite du Bois that I sample in a Beverly Hills department store while delivering a DVD to an actor for possible narration in my documentary.

Not allowed upstairs at the Hollywood talent agency, and still needing to add a note, I seek out a place to jot one. I descend a floor to find at the end of a long hallway, a barbershop with a small floral print couch in the reception area. With permission, I sit a moment. An animated and attractive hairstylist comes by and strikes up a conversation. Soon I am hearing about his own long time documentary project, a film about the famous Hollywood hairdresser, Jay Sebring. Sebring was a revolutionary of men's styling for clients like Jim Morrison, Steve McQueen, Dennis Hopper and Elvis Presley. Sebring, along with his dear friend Sharon Tate, was murdered by Manson and followers, on a bloody August night.

The hairstylist I am talking to wants to redeem his uncle's name from the media frenzy that celebrated Manson while vilifying his kin.

The actor will pass on this project, but my voice will end up working well for narration after all. And all it was! - a difficult and frustrating day of recording the voice over with plains flying overhead, boardwalk ruckus, barking dogs, and thumping neighbors above my tourist attraction Venice boardwalk apartment. We huddle in my bedroom against the back wall reading off Red Reign's narration lines, heart wrenching and dire:

'In 2002, a witness, an armed police guard, working for the public security system, participated in illegal arrests and torture of Falun Gong practitioners. He gave this first-hand account about a female practitioner. He said, 'She had wounds and scars covering her entire body after a week of severe torment and forced food intake. Then, while left fully conscious, given no anesthetics, whatsoever, they cut her chest with a scalpel. Blood gushed out. She shouted out in pain, saying, 'Falun Gong

is great.' Then she said, 'You killed me; one individual. You won't kill us all.' At that moment, the doctor hesitated...but he continued to do the veins. The heart was carved out, first, then the kidneys. When her cardiac veins were cut by the scissors, she started twitching. It was extremely horrible. It sounded like something was being ripped apart. Her mouth and her eyes were wide open. I don't want to continue.'

I didn't want to continue. It was a difficult day, an emotional day. Finn's strength and firmness proved valuable and yet challenging to my raw senses.

Finn and I, nonetheless will be pleasantly surprised at the results when we upload the audio files later that day at the cafe.

I start trusting that this project is directing me more than I am directing it, trusting my process in art and of life, trusting that I will understand why I am just three degrees separation from Charles Manson.

I ponder on Sharon Tate's husband, French born Roman Polansky.

Roman Polanski is a filmmaker form Paris, home of my metaphoric ancestors, and a Polish Jew, place of my biological ancestry. He is a child during a genocide, the Holocaust, where many Jews, Gypsies and vulnerable perish.

And one day, a Jew and a Gypsy, Finn, and myself, will make a movie about a genocide, championing the vulnerable.

So ghosts remain as they do for Polanski.

Some will become the living/walking dead, yet others use the whole of their lives to redeem the dead and the ghosts they carry, remembering, honoring, transforming them through art and action.

Living in Los Angeles seems to truncate the idea of 'six degrees of separation' first introduced by Frigyes Karinthy, down to a mere three, or often just one degree.

How am I connected to Hungarian Frigyes Karinthy? Connected by profession (we are both writers), by astrological or blood type, (both Cancers) geography, geology? By mission or vision, passion, fashion, religion, decisions?

Invisible threads.

'An invisible red thread connects those who are destined to meet regardless of time, place or circumstance. The thread may stretch or tangle but will never break.' Says a Chinese Proverb

Turning, or returning, to my own biological lineage, affirming the unexplored facets of my spiritual nature, I begin the quest to reconcile other infamous chasms or what Carl Jung might call archetypes, in a process he calls alchemy.

Weaving my threads:

Pierre and Marthe,
Herman and Renee,
Narcissus and Goldman.

With those yet to come:

Rodin, Rose and Camille,
Lilith and Eve.

Rational and intuitive,
Love and freedom,
Ich und du. I and Thou,
Fisheyes and Pearls.

Four portraits from my blood line~

Gert:
My grandmother Gertrude, or *Gitle* in her native tongue, meaning good, and grandfather Sam, were both very much from the 'old country'; I knew would never survive without each other. And it was so.

Every evening they sat at the formica kitchen table together, while she expertly peeled and sliced apples that they would share in exquisite rapport. She would pass him a slice between her thumb and the knife's blade, an apron across her round sack of potatoes body, their custom every evening.

They lived on the green line- not far from the Boston University campus, so I made brief appearances after class and she would wonder why I dressed like a gypsy and ate like a rabbit.

'I don't understand, when I grew up all I ate was some greens that grew by the house,' she tells me, suspicious of my then macrobiotic diet.
"But that *is* macrobiotic!" I explain.

When Mr. Kaye gives my painting class a portrait assignment, I take a sketchbook and pastels and ask *Bubbe*, grandmother, to sit for me. I portray her round smooth face with warm tones, purples around the creased eyes, wearing a white blouse flecked with primary colors.

Professor K, who wears a button down blue coat,

notoriously blunt and critical, hates it and grades it a C- , too warm, too glowy he grumbles. He clearly doesn't know her.

The portrait gets framed and hangs in their apartment all the same.

Gert has a bad heart and will need surgery. She, who grew up without a mother or shoes as a poor farm girl in Poland, is terrified and strongly opposes the operation.

She gets her way and dies only hours before the next day's scheduled surgery. When I see her at the hospital that last night, she has a pleading expression on her face, a ventilator taped to her face.

I never see her again.

Sam:
Zaide, grandfather in Yiddish, always wearing a dark overcoat regardless of season, is sparse with words- except to tell a joke or to convey some bit of anecdotal wisdom He answers the phone exuberantly, then quickly passes it on to my grandmother, Bubbe.

A dedicated assistant in the synagogue across the street, he is there faithfully everyday, handing out prayer books to all who enter. His father and his son are both rabbis. But his is a place of humble service in between them, supporting his older brothers in their esteemed professions.

When my chatty grandmother dies early that winter, the taciturn man begins to talk. A lot. He doesn't stop. Not until that summer, when he dies of stomach cancer, six months hence.

While he is in the hospital, I am asked to go and sketch his portrait, too. Having absorbed the reprimanding from my teacher, Mr. K, of my grandmother's portrait, I am careful to portray my grandfather with great accuracy, unsentimental.

When I am done, he asks to see it.

I hold up the rendering from my chair at the foot of his bed.

He shudders, gasps and jolts to one side, stunned by gray Lucian Freud skin tones drawn over a gaunt structure, horrified by the mirroring image before him.

Embarrassed by my skills, which now seem only haughty and insolent, I petrify from guilt and shame.

Maybe Mr. K would have graded me favorably, but I have failed.

'Its Okay." My grandfather retracts having digested the reality. Then, in his love and wisdom responds, "Sometimes you just have to tell it like it is.'

He dies shortly thereafter, late July, my father's birthday.

He has given me this gift -permission to tell the truth even when it's painful.

I never forget the sting of his reaction. Perhaps it will later inform my choices while making RED REIGN, the gruesome truth will be told with great care for the viewer, but the truth will be told nonetheless.

The press release will read, *'Red Reign examines the shocking evidence of forced organ harvesting of China's prisoners of conscience, the practitioners of Falun Gong. Filmmaker Masha Savitz zeroes in on the efforts of Nobel Prize nominee David Matas, who wrote the book 'Bloody Harvest: The Killing of Falun Gong.' David Kilgour, a former member of the Canadian Parliament, alleged that Falun Gong prisoners were being killed in order to harvest their organs for the lucrative government-run organ transplant business.'*

Syd:
My maternal grandparents lived in a Payne's Gray ranch house on Oxford Street in New York. I am in art school when my grandmother Sadie, who prefers to be called Syd, falls into a coma from an aneurism.

She likes me to choose outfits for her when I am ten years old and visiting her in Florida, matching blouses with slacks and accessories.

I most enjoy raiding her storage closets for vintage coats and dresses which I love to wear. She is amused that a teenager finds her old discarded clothes so appealing- a floral print dress with rhinestones around the neckline and scattered around the body of the frock, a fur lined mocha colored jacket, purple stripy sandals, a black cocktail dress with sheer draping around the shoulders and neck line. I have a photo of myself wearing it, together with a yellowing photo of her from the 60's in the same dress. She is posing in front of a portrait of herself over the piano.

My peers often ask to borrow my wardrobe for costumes for school plays and other themed events. 'But these are my regular clothes!' I wince at this request.

It's early spring and I am terrified for the funeral. What if I don't cry, something nearly impossible for me to do since my brother became fatally ill when I was twelve years old. If I don't cry the family will know that I am cold after all, cold and detached, a position I am apointeded in my adolescence.

If I don't cry, maybe they're right about me. Maybe I *am* cold and unfeeling. This would certainly confirm it. I am panicked.

The night before the funeral I stay with my grandfather in their home on the golf course in Westchester so that he will not be alone.

That morning is cool and rainy.

Grandpa Lou offers me Grandma's galoshes.

'No thanks Grandpa, I'm Okay' I decline.

'You should really wear the galoshes.' He holds them up to display.

'No, really, I am fine.'

He snickers and walks away.

The service takes place.
Tears fall.
Relief.

We are driving to the cemetery. I ride with my dad in the front seat. My mother is with her siblings in the limousine. The sun breaks through the rain clouds with a spectacular display. I had always seen my mother as emotional, at times, uncomfortable by her emotive nature. She is known to cry at commercials. Now my father is telling me that I'm just like her. WHAT? He tells me that when they began to date she never showed emotion. It wasn't until years later, that she became emotional.

We get to the cemetery. I gather with the large extended family around the gravesite. As the burial ceremony concludes, everyone disperses heading to their cars. I feel myself inch closer to the grave. I don't want to leave her. A surge of irrational grief overtakes me.

'I can't leave her here by herself.'

I am sobbing.

'I can't leave her here, I don't want to leave her.'
As if from slightly above, I see myself, hands cupping my face, amazed at this extreme and rather out-of-control dramatic behavior, and think, 'How wonderful!'

Each of my parents swiftly clutches one of my arms and leads me out of the cemetery.

My grandfather, Lou, remarks to my oldest cousin, leaning into her ear, 'I told her she should have worn Grandma's galoshes.'

Lou:
My grandfather on my mother's side is Lou. The old-

est of fourteen children, though only twelve survive to adulthood, is proud and forthright, sometimes cruel in his comments. 'You gained weight, your ass looks big.' He is strict and if you leave your shoes in the wrong place you will hear about it. Everyone will.

When he dies, my father eulogizes him demonstrating the mastery of his rabbi craft- my father tells the truth about Lou, the man who was always antagonistic towards him, but in a way that leaves everyone appreciating his cantankerous nature, smiling with wry affection, 'Oh that was Grandpa alright.' There is a great opportunity for healing as the conflicted and difficult feelings are transmuted by the shared experience of those in attendance. Ah, the power of language, words, intention.

I am on my way home from college for winter break. I stop to visit grandpa where I spend a rare few hours alone with him. He asks me when I am going to give up painting, did I have a date in mind, a plan for abandoning ship, renouncing life as an artist?

In the kitchen he tells me that when he was a young man in Europe, he was offered a scholarship to study art. He goes down to the basement to retrieve an elegant pen and ink drawing of a figure, portrait that he made as a young man.

'Art school? You want to be an artist like those men in white flouncy shirts with long billowy sleeves who sit at the cafe all day?' his father, my great grandfather, had harangued him.

Lou becomes a business owner of a pharmacy with the Americanized family name on the awning, and passes on the same limitations to my mother, who comes home to tell him one day that she wants to be an artist. 'An artist? Absolutely not - you can be an art teacher.' He tells her.

She gets her degree in art education, something she would never use.
This all begins to explain a lot.

I had always been encouraged to follow my creative nature, encouraged to apply to art school, so I am completely dismayed when on Thanksgiving of my junior year, time to declare a major, the conversation goes like this:

'Have you made a decision about a major?' My parents ask eagerly at the holiday table.

'Painting.' I answer.
'That's not a decision', my mother quips sharply.

As the conversation with grandfather continues, I recognize the line of artistic leanings and the parental thwarting, which has now come to me like an ancestral karmic relay. It is my chance to take the baton, pass it, or break the cycle and use it to conduct a symphony, or as a magic wand.

After hours of Lou trying to convince me to give up painting that winter night, it is time for me to leave. We are standing at his front door, in a last attempt he asks, 'So when are you going to give up painting?'

'I am too talented to give up painting, Grandpa.'

He throws back his head, letting out the heartiest laugh of delight.

There is a bridge that Pierre and Marthe could not build, but that I must. Then traverse, or become.

It won't be for many years until I realize that I will also have to reconcile the shattered life of sculptor Camille Claudel, Rodin's lover, and all other women artists like her, like us, a story once too frightening to approach, now my mission.

How to begin?

Like most of the human species, in a tug-o-war

between opposing selves, my Leonean dramatic ascendant and a Cancer Moon, shy and receding, checks and balances, limits and expansion, aspects of opposites, like South node in Sagittarius, my wild untamed self, and a North Node in Gemini, calling me to refine and communicate. So, I will fall in love with a refined and wild Sag communicator. I protect my fierce need for both an independent and creative life, while taming a desire for love and intimacy.

Once I understand the gap between Pierre the artist, and Marthe the wife and model, I reflect on the ways that I am them.

It is years later, while writing at the cafe on a rainy January afternoon, that I will smile with the sublime realization that I AM EVERYONE.

After writing the story about Marthe and Pierre, I never make another self-portrait.

Painting created the bridge from a non verbal reality. I owe my life and deepest joys to painting. But, it is through the written word that I communicate specific ideas. It is verbal language that yields insights into the nature of my existence, offering access into worlds, both my own and ones I will create.

Through writing I can explore and share my emotional and spiritual inheritance.
Although, I had occasionally wondered if I should

become a rabbi, the notion always left as quickly as it came. But, this time it persists.

I know that this five year graduate program will require gymnast like hoop jumping.

Should I jump the many hoops academically, religiously, socially?

I am thinking about this on the way home from dinner at a friend's house when I come across a card lying on the ground in the street. The card has just one word written upon it .'Jump.' I do.

I am off to the seminary.

I have been an artist, like my mother, embracing form and color, Aphrodite of prismatic expression. And now I will travel my father's path as clergy. Service, in neutral austere colors and cerebral inquiry like the two different paths of Herman Hesse's, *Narcissus and Goldman*. One a holy man, scholarly Narcissus of father sky, and the other, Goldman, pursuing the experience of mother earth's sensual offerings.

On Finn's recommendation, I read *Narcissus and Goldman*, which will elucidate the polarities within me. I reflect both of the characters in this story of two men who meet at a cloister in medieval Europe. They develop a profound friendship, but their different temperaments take them on different life courses, though they are always united by their commitment to experiencing their true nature fully.

And it will lead me to alchemy.

"Art was a union of the father and mother worlds, of mind and blood. It might start in utter sensuality and lead to total abstraction; then again it might originate in pure concept and end in bleeding flesh. Any work of art that was truly sublime, not just a good juggler's trick; that was filled with the eternal secret, like the master's Madonna; every obviously genuine work of art had this dangerous, smiling double face, was male-female, a merging of instinct and pure spirituality." ~ Hesse

This story articulates my past and portends my future, as does many of the recommendations from this friend. My close connection with Finn will prevail as pivotal.

Because after duality would come consummation.

CHAPTER TWO

art war love porn

Perhaps it is the mounting pressure of Saturn in the eighth house, ruling birth death power sex, taking the form of an impotent marriage, fueling and catapulting me across the patchwork of states to the shores of the other ocean. The ringed planet completing its return around my natal chart. The opportunity for reinvention, as my friend Pamela constantly educates me on the choreography of the planets and their dance in our lives.

In those days, either protesting my circumstance, attempting retaliation or redemption, I paint what some would later call, to my horror, malady and regret, 'porn.'

My ex-soldier husband, W, suffering from Post-Traumatic Stress Disorder, a term I don't yet know, and a litany of other textbook dysfunctions, all well earned, refrains from any display of affection towards me, and it seems, it was only me.

He hands me a copy of 'To Know A Woman', by Amos Oz, one of the few books I read is an unsettling account of an Israeli espionage agent who retires following his wife's accidental death.'

Was this intended as a warning, a call for help, foreshadowing?

I was naïve then, a trait that drew him towards me.

The thought that he works for the Mossad always remains in the back of my mind.

) ((●)) (

We were opposites attracting. But the color wheel and color theory teaches me a truth about this 'opposites attract' dynamic.

Opposite colors, that is, complimentary colors, together can be bold, pop, all contrast. Varoom! But, when mixed together however, they will eventually create flat gray.

Orange mixed with blue will neutralize the orange

detracting from its vibrancy. And so it goes with all complimentary colors.

It seems to me the ideal romantic match is one in which the combination creates a third color.

The primaries, when combined, create a secondary. A mate should share similar interests and qualities, but also have a set very different.

Yellow and blue make green, red and yellow, orange, and red and blue produce purple.

An ideal couple will each vibrate at its own frequency, yet create something together–a family, a business, a dynasty, a farm, a home, garden, foundation, a movie.

Or all of the above.

Like Tanna and Henry, from collaborations further colors can be formed. Blue-Violet, Red-Violet, Red-Orange, Yellow-Orange, Yellow-Green, Blue-Green.

Pairing with another that is too similar will not ignite dynamism or foster growth, even in the re-creation of self. Then again, a field full of daisy's is resplendent. Monochromatic and homogenous has its place, but not so much with creators.

He didn't speak as a child, W tells me, he refused. No medical reason, just sheer will.

What makes an infant decide to withhold communication while other babies live to please and bond, imitating their parents' sounds and gestures with coos, gurgles and giggles?

He withholds love, communication, connection.

He has twenty-five years to perfect this modus operandi. I don't have a chance.

W uses the silence tactic with me as well, punishing me for days at a time without explanation. This experience teaches me that to enter the mind of a mad person, in hopes of understanding them, is to tread on madness oneself.

I imagine the weeks before he is born, ingesting the bitter waters of his mother's womb, cortisol flooding her frail system. The young woman, a survivor of the Holocaust, miscarries five other children that cannot remain in the amniotic fluid of terror. But he is different, fierce and strong, and would grow and thrive on code red distress.

W is born with penetrating teal eyes and with a bad taste in his mouth, a bitterness that becomes part of his constitution and orientation. He will grow addicted to the adrenalin release, to the flavor of chaos, only exacerbated as a soldier.

He refuses speech for his first five years. His father, Joseph, a linguist mastering many languages, translates books. So, in spite, W rejects language.

His mother, Riza, is controlling and needy. So W refuses to need her, or anyone else and is irate when she needs him.

Riza has neglected to care for him, spending all her time at the hospital bed of his father, her dying husband, who slowly deteriorates from war wounds.

After Josephs's death, Riza attempts suicide.
Social services will intervene when a teacher finds young W stealing an apple from another child- he has no lunch.

I first meet W on a farm in Israel where his foster mother lives. She, a spirited petite dark haired woman, with a collection of pine cones and other natural treasures that she turns into decorative crafts, animals and such, cheerfully displayed on a table in her modest house. She had lost a son in an accident, but gained a foster son in W.

'I want him to ask me to marry him.' I tell my sister before I even know his name.

This falls into the category of lessons called- be careful

what you ask for.

He moves to Boston and in with me.

Eager to make him feel welcomed and part of my circle, I encourage him to spend time with all of my friends which he will take to a nefarious level. This act of good faith will turn on me as seeds of suspicion and mistrust are first planted here.

Our second year is contentious.

He gets a call that his mother is dying, her condition, more advanced than he knew.

'Do you want me to come with you?' I ask, as he needs to fly back to Israel right away.

'You don't need to come.'

'I know. But if you want me to come, I will.'
'Yes, I want you to come.'

Turbulent weeks follow.
My parents had planned a trip abroad. We take the next plane from the East Coast. We are on the same flight as my parents. They bring my grandmother's engagement ring, 'Just in case.' My mother said.

Although I can speak basic conversation, asking the time and ordering a cup of coffee, *eem filter,* or falafel *bevakasha*, please, my Hebrew skills are not suitable for the delicate circumstances of picking up subtle clues and cues in a hospital, and during serious conversations regarding visas and embassies.

A social worker helping with Riza concludes that W and I need to get married for his visa.

Outside the hospital room W puts the ring on my finger.

'Aren't you going to ask me?'

'Only wimps ask.'

I'm engaged.

) ((●)) (

I rub scented cool white hand cream onto the effete hands of my soon to be mother in law.

I spread out the sheet onto the bed thinking, 'the unfolding, this is the unfolding.'

T h e u n f o l d i n g.

The stress filled days are spent managing medical

emergencies. Riza needs oxygen or falls out of bed. There are tense Visa related trips to the embassy in Tel Aviv. Everything is slipping out of my grasp in foreign tongue and on foreign soil.

I am a minor character in the wedding that is being planned- my own.

Trying to be supportive, I lilt, powerless, swept up in a force I can't quell as I am given a mauve lace dress to wear at the nuptials.

With bearings lost, I have lost my north and track of time.

We are out buying flowers for the ceremony. It's the day of the wedding. It suddenly occurs to me- it is April 1!

A fantastic cosmic April fools joke. W and I agree. We will laugh silently under the *chupah* canopy.

I can relax, appreciating the humor amidst crisis and trepidation for a moment, one sun filled moment picking out flowers at the farmers market this early spring.

Following the fool's day wedding, I return to he USA and to work.

Riza dies the next day. W, still awaiting his visa, is called back into the military reserves and back into active duty. He doesn't tell me. He fears it will make him vulnerable. Instead, I am.

When he arrives into my life months later, he is full of soldiers' secrets, burdens, and restlessness.

The complicated resentment toward his mother transfers to me like debt, my inheritance along with some gold and diamond jewelry.

This combination is a one-two punch.

I'm out, but stumble back to my feet.

To Pearl Paint, an arts supply store around the corner from my Prospect Street studio.

Using Gamblin's silver, black and all shades blue- Ultramarine, Prussian, Cobalt - I paint myself in silhouette with army boots floating above my head, titled, 'Black and Blue.'

The next painting is large, red and black, female body-parts and army boots in sectioned boxes - 'Dreams from the Front Lines.'

'V is for vortex, vagina, velocity- the shape your army boots make in the corner of the room,' I scribble in my journal by our bed where he has a carving knife protruding from the floor boards in case of intruders- what I have become to him.

He casually informs me one day that the smell of gunpowder can make a man aroused, that this was a well known fact.

It was Alchemist Wei Boyang, of the Eastern Han dynasty, who was the first known person to have documented the chemical composition of gunpowder. Ironicaly, the Toaist lived secluded in the mountains, spending his life creating an elixir for immortality. The yin and the yang.

W calls escalators 'moving flight' and mixes up prepositions saying, 'I worked my butt out.' He can make me laugh when I'm not limp, with my life force spinning in reverse.

I refer to him as 'Hyperbole Man'- extremely good looking, extremely smart, extremely charming, and extremely intense with a tendency toward extreme hostility and a perpetual craving for cortisol in mouth and blood. His or another's.

) ((●)) (

Despite the fact that we had every state-of the-art device, cell phones, pagers, etc., with which to communicate, there must first be the desire to reach, know, and touch another. Otherwise it's useless, flamboyant, insulting.

With cell phone, computer, home line, work line, he is impossible to reach. Because when one wants to be accessible, telepathy will do just fine. And sometimes the best way to communicate is still a smile. A hug. Listening.

I have the desire to connect on primordial levels, but will need to assimilate hard drives, learn aperture settings, understand the components and function of treatments (a screenplay blueprint), log lines, by lines, and tag lines, which will increase my face lines, as foretold in my palm's life line. All with the hope and belief that it is possible to surpass the delineating lines of our existence, transcend the edges, reach beyond the delimited boundaries of me, my, skin, I.

New lexicons to learn, playing matchmaker to form and content as I will later try to make sense, and art of this story, in the unfamiliar language and structure of screenwriting which begins with FADE IN.

I will introduce scenes with terms like INT., interior or EXT., exterior.

But, this is my interior attempting to become exterior, sculpted into the shape of story, chiseled with the likeness of humanity, polished to the sheen of grace and redemption. At least this is the idea.

) ◖ (●) ◗ (

Screenplay:

BLOOD of EDEN

EXT. NEIGHBOR'S BACKYARD, LATE AFTERNOON

Young neighborhood kids are playing in the yard of a suburban middle-class home, there is laughter and joyful shrieks as they chase each other through October leaves.

A little spotted dog, tied to a tree with a chain, is barking.

One of the young girls, Maggie, five years old, with pig tails, moves slowly towards the dog.

The other kids form a semi circle behind her.

LITTLE BOY
Don’t go near Toughie, he’ll bite you, ya know.

In slow motion she keeps moving toward the jumping dog.

OLDER GIRL
Yea, don’t go near Toughie....

Maggie has a determined air of calm assuredness, knowing just what he needs.

LITTLE MAGGIE
(Voice Over-audience hears)
He just needs love.

In the background the kids continue to shout in protest, warning her.

She is unmoved and steadfast, approaching the barking dog in slow motion.

Toughie leaps up growling and bites

her on the hand.

The kids react with surprised faces, outbursts, laughter, and pointing.

She covers her wounded and bleeding hand to minimize any evidence of her betrayal while holding back tears.

INT. DOCTOR'S OFFICE. DAY

The girl is sitting on the examining table, her Mom watching on.

The doctor prepares a tetanus shot. Maggie stoically prepares for her immanent fate.
As the shot is administered, the pain and humiliation are too much to bear-betrayed by love.

She lets out a mournful howl.

CLOSE UP OF GIRL CRYING CROSS FADES TO:

25 years later-
INT. LOFT. BATHROOM

Maggie is cleaning the bathroom. She is wearing an old black slip, barefoot, a scarf holds her hair back pirate-style. She is scrubbing the old claw-foot bathtub and singing along to the background music, Seal's CRAZY.

She finds a stack of magazines under the tub.
Soberly, she opens the pages and stares blankly at the pages before her.

She sits on the lip of the tub pausing with the discovery.

INT. DOORWAY. EVENING

Maggie waits at the door while Ron comes home from work- She plans to scare him playfully when he walks in the front door.

MAGGIE
Boo!

He has her up against the wall in a split second ready to break the neck of the invading thief.

He realizes it's Maggie.

RON
Never do that again.

Do you understand?
Never.. do.. that
again.

He walks away leaving her there against the wall stunned.

INT. BATHROOM. NIGHT
Ron is in the shower and Maggie is washing up at the sink.

MAGGIE
Hey Ron

No answer, silence.

RON
Yeah? What?

MAGGIE
Ya know when I was
cleaning, I found a
bunch of magazines...

RON
Yeah...the guys at
work gave them to me.

MAGGIE
So you don't mind if

I throw them out…

Ron grunts indifferently.

INT. KITCHEN. DAY

Maggie tosses the magazines into the garbage.

INT. BEDROOM. DAY

While changing the sheets, Maggie finds more magazines under his side of the bed.

INT. STUDIO. NEXT DAY.

Maggie is talking on the phone while she gessoes new canvases in the studio.

LIZZIE

Well his sun squares your 8th house planets!

MAGGIE

I don't feel like I can tell him he can't look at this stuff, I'm not the mind police, that's

the CCP's job! At
the same time, I know
this is destroying
us.

LIZZIE
As long as he has
this outlet, a
disembodied woman,
he doesn't need to
deal with a real one,
and Maggie, you are a
real one alright.

Maggie sighs.

INT. LOFT STUDIO. DAY

She stares at the warped images in the magazine.

Maggie methodically squeezes slippery color from tubes of paint in systematic order around the glass palette: warm yellows, oranges ochre, reds and alizarin crimson, the purples, and cool blues.

She mixes a solution of turpentine and linseed oil in a jar and sits an old can of brushes, and rags.

With conviction, she begins to paint the images in the magazine, huge, on a mission.

She paints a large scale image impressionistically with warm colors, pink, lavender, oranges...

) ((●)) (

Discovering stacks of porn magazines hidden while I clean the house, something W doesn't count on happening too frequently, I confront him with the unsettling findings.

I approach him awkwardly. W is busy on the computer in the spare room.

"The guys at work gave them to me," he shrugs. He doesn't lift his head from the computer screen.

"So, you don't mind if I throw them out?"

"No, go ahead," eyes fixed ahead.

I toss out a pile, only to find a new crop hidden behind my dresser or under the claw foot tub.

Sitting on the tub rim with magazine in hand, I study

the images with fierce concentration, transfixed, feeling into each pixel for information.
Women in mini nurse uniforms. Where are they? Are they numb to feeling at all, or are feelings submerged like fault lines, or do they spark on the surface, a fire hazard?

What does a collection of these images do to a man's mind, to his heart?

Do connecting sinews get severed between the two?

I wonder what he sees when he looks at me.

He won't talk to me. Only lies, excuses and blame, blaming me to keep the focus off of him. So, I go off spinning and loosing my center.
Rumination on indignation.
Limit fantasy?

It seems absurd, but it is undermining an already fragile, tested, and battered marriage.

Where is the root of this poisonous plant and what is the poison's antidote?

There is only one thing to do. I bring the magazines to my studio, determined to make the cold and detached images of women and coitus as beautiful as possible. This mission to (re)elevate and hallow sex leads me on a journey that will last years.

I layer paint.

I bring the first painting home- four ft' by four ft' of warm orange, pink and violet glowing penetration that I will hang in the living room directly across from the front door entrance.

W comes home that night and never responds.

Months pass.

No response.

Everyone else certainly does.

He has still not responded.

BLOOD OF EDEN, Continued

INT. GALLERY, NIGHT

Bartender is serving complimentary glasses of wine.

Ron looks handsome and is charming Maggie's friends. He plays this role in public well.

Gwen, Maggie's sister, is there with her husband. She clings to him, feel-ing out of her element, compensating by drinking lots of wine.

There are strong and mixed reactions to the art exhibition. We are looking down into the crowd from above.

Facial expressions show, hands to mouth, eyebrows raise, hands on hips, beard stroked, smirks, grins, giggles, throats clear.

CROWD
Oh, ooh.

An attractive woman, 30's. is whispering to a female friend beside her.

WOMAN
You know, I have been raped, and these paintings are very healing to me.

MAN IN HIS 50'S
Very erotic, provocative.

ANDROGYNOUS WOMAN
These paintings are violent.

ASIAN MAN
So Aggressive.

WOMAN
(in a white turban)
Holy.

) ((●)) (

Over time, the painting series I will eventually name Come/Union, becomes as much an exploration of visual relationships as human relationships. Are there negative spaces, what is the space between them? Are their edges boldly defined or an ambiguous merging of color and flesh, are these tones similar or contrasting?

How do the elements relate?
The compositions of only genitals in the act of intercourse fill the space of the canvas.

There are no faces to convey expressions, no indication of age, no context nor clues as to whether this depiction of making love is making a baby, or make up sex.
Is this a one-night stand, a man with a mistress, a woman with a student, lovers reuniting after many years, a rape, or silver wedding anniversary?

No paraphernalia, just penetration.

I paint with two intentions- represent male and female balanced on the canvas, and make it beautiful, as I will try to do in life. But paint is easier to move then civilization.

I research Tantric culture, which employs sacred sexuality as a form of cultivation to get closer to the Divine, evoking the divine in self and in the partner. Conversely, sexuality in our society seems to move us further away from divinity, from the self and other, twisting ideas of Tantrism to feed and engorge lust, greed, detachment, inadequacy, competition, I could go on forever. I almost do.

Once, invited to a Hindu ceremony, a Puja, celebrating erotic love, I observe how the appropriation perpetuates discontent- the desire for 'soul mate', the 'one.' More workshops to attend, more ways to wet the collective appetite, more ways to inflict a sense of not enough.

'I want to worship the goddess in you', says a well presented man at the event.

Which goddess is that, I wonder, Kali? She will turn you into a three headed toad.

Or Hestia, who focuses on her inner sanctuary as a Virgin Goddess? Yes, worship at her temple!

It would feel more truthful had he made some direct sexual advance, no matter how crude.

Sacred language to cover up lust is rather revolting. Sad for the poor searching souls.

When I get home that night, I feel as if I had been contaminated by some pervasive collective darkness. I have. But, it calls itself light. Neon flashing red.

Such is my quest for understanding the nature of intimacy, with Chiron and Saturn in the eighth house, suggesting a deep inquiry and a healing of the issues of sex, death and things hidden.

A Korean stock trader tells me he thinks my paintings are aggressive.

Jules thinks I just paint penises. People read many things into the paintings which seems to reveal more about themselves - but they will be projected onto me.

I hadn't counted on such reactions. Interesting, sure, but I seem to be producing, in many cases, the opposite of my intention. This seems to be backfiring.

Instead of creating harmony and balance between the sexes, I must recognize how single I am in my personal life.

The act of making the paintings only affirms the reality as I surround myself with grand and vivid odes to union.

Is art a consolation prize for misery, or is misery just the price?

Before I leave Boston I find a book, 'The Woman Who Slept with Men To Take The War Out of Them.'

Though dyslexic and disinclined to reading, I inherit my fathers love of books, and the pleasure of prowling bookstores, drawn to image, font, running my hands over covers, feeling the texture of the book jacket against my responsive fingers. I too am seduced by books and collect them. And sometimes I even read one. I don't get too far with this one however, but I do enjoy the title, and imagine the contents...

I grow to understand many things from what I don't read, and what is not said.

Like things not said by the husband, product of policies set by men who are also suckled on cortisol, acting from fear, which sometimes looks like pride or protection.

'Jacob was left alone, and a man wrestled with him till daybreak. When the man saw that he could not overpower him, he touched the socket of Jacob's hip so that his hip was wrenched as he wrestled with the man. Then the man said, 'Let me go, for it is daybreak.'

But Jacob replied, 'I will not let you go unless you bless me.' The man asked him, 'What is your name?'

'Jacob,' He answered. Then the man said, 'Your name will no longer be Jacob, but Israel, because you have struggled with God and with humans and have overcome.'

Changing the name of one who is sick to confuse the angel of death grants good fortune. Name changes appear often in the Jewish tradition.

Perhaps a new name, a renewed identity, can be considered for Yisrael (Israel) meaning: struggles with

God, to Yizrachel, meaning 'Shines light with God.'

Some change their names to change their fate, or too, according to the Talmud, a change of address can bring a change of luck.

I am changing address.

This time, from Kendel Street, Cambridge Massachusetts to Carleton Street, Berkeley, California.

Because, after the marriage ends, there is work to be done, or perhaps more precisely, ease to be experienced, repose to be relished, levity lived.

If my first love had broken my heart, the marriage broke my spirit. Others will later break my faith, will and hope, respectively. But, I will become accustomed to moving through life with the broken bits, precariously balancing my body to keep the shattered parts in place- certainly not alone in this jangled posture. It may be a comment on our culture, or merely the mark of humankind.

And when there is nothing left to break, except stubborn patterns, I will turn into light and radiate, and this is probably the purpose all along.

) ((●)) (

A Tarot card pulled at the wooden kitchen table in my Cambridge apartment depicts a woman in a lilac colored lake- the Star Card, portending hot tubs and the scenic seascapes of Northern California. Though hard to imagine at the time, I will later recall the card in a hot tub on a February night surrounded by lush gardens under a starry canopy in a Berkeley backyard, northern California.

Three months prior, I visit college friends, Sila in Oakland and my dorm roommate Belle, now Sila's roommate. Sitting at an outdoor table at Café Mediterranean, I perceive a message clear as Genesis's Abraham, '*Lech l'cha,* Go forth.' There is a window that will not remain open for long. Here is a place I can recuperate and recreate. Go forth. So, I move to Berkeley.

In this crystalline moment, I finish the last sip of the

cafe au-lait, and saunter down Telegraph Avenue to a vintage clothing shop.

With my 'Boston clothes' stuffed into the black and neon pink plastic bag, I exit the shop, donning my new old garments which resemble my old old clothes in every way, yet feeling thoroughly altered, unencumbered. Free.

While in San Francisco's Deloris Park I wander into a knife store where knives line the paint chipped walls of this dimly lit building. Seeing no one behind the counter, a brief moment of dread overtakes me, gory scenarios irrupt.

Uncharacteristically, I buy my soon to be ex-husband an antique sword decoratively engraved along the blade. He has always been fascinated with weapons, I have always been fearful of them.

Now I need one to cut our chords, cut my losses.

In other dimensions I wield a sword but have forgotten all this- it would be a few years before I will begin to remember who I really am.

I try to remember.

According to a myth, before we are born, an angel taps us on the top lip to wipe clean our memory that we forget from where we came- the reason for the small indentation between our top lip.

I am compelled to know my true self, separate from social conventions and conditions, so when I move into my first apartment near Kenmore Square, endeavoring to act free of predisposition, I refrain from mechanically organizing according to norms. Instead, I place cleaners on the top shelf, the canned goods under the sink, my clothes are stacked in milk crates.

I come to find however, that sometimes there is acumen to be gleaned in things tried and tested.

This would begin the long and arduous process of sorting out which was which.

Wisdom, perhaps?

Not yet wise, I'm living out a Clash song.

W feels betrayed by those he has loved, so he pushes me away, testing me, protecting himself. If I leave, it confirms his notion that you can't trust anyone and he will always be betrayed. If I stay, his respect for me will erode, for I must be weak and put up with the abuse, which will make the abuse more severe. I betray myself.

Street smart and culturally savvy Lorraine, a friend from Boston, with teased black hair and red lipstick, who appears on page twenty-one of Nan Goldin, the famed still photographer's collection, The Ballad of Sexual Dependency, puts W's Alder Wood acoustic guitar in my hands and teaches me three chords.

I'm lit, composing songs that sound Nashville born, despite having no exposure or particular interest in this genre or style.

At this point I am still struggling with 'Should I stay or should I go?' regarding W.

I am hanging on. Hanging in. Hanging.
I'm the hanged one.

I write a song. Chords E, D, A

Hanged Man.

Trying to untangle
or is it to uncleave
from everything I've held on to
with clenched tiger teeth

Anticipating separating
from all that I have known
to be your loving wife
or to be on my own?

I'm suspended, new perspective,
As I'm swinging in the breeze,
everything looks different now
way up here in the trees.

(Chorus)
I'm the hanged one the unnamed one.
and I'm hanging in a deck of tarot cards.
I'm the hanged one the unnamed one.
and I'm hanging
in a deck of tarot cards.

The Empress is full of grace,
the Fool very dear,
the devil keeps us in chains
paralyzed by fear
I'm the hanged one the unnamed one.
and I'm hanging
in a deck of tarot cards.

But me I'm surrendering
to a life gone in reverse
to what can be called rebirth
some would say a blessed thing
and some would say a curse

So as death comes
a breath comes
that fills my lungs a new
with pure possibility
of all that I might do

(Chorus)
I'm the hanged one
the unnamed one.
and I'm hanging
in a deck of tarot cards.
I'm the hanged, count the pain one

unashamed one
defamed one
renamed one
blamed
un tamed

Reinvention resurrection
I have another chance,
before this song is over
and before the last dance.

A mournful steel guitar to accompany lyrics.

Ooooo, steeeel gutar.

I sing, write and paint, but I can't always talk.

To silence me, to keep me from asking or stating, W's first tactic is anger. It usually works. As a backup, he resorts to shame and guilt.

Shame tells me that I am incompetent, unintelligent, undesirable.
Guilt says, 'If you leave me, I have no one.'
Ouch! That usually slays me.

But, one day I softly utter, 'That doesn't seem a good reason to stay married.'

Guilt fails. Truth prevails. Karma paid. Spell broken.

After years of exhausting myself to make the marriage work and then trying to end it, because he resists me on both efforts, I will finally, while reading a Buddhist inspired book on my Green-line commute to work, disengage and politely go about living my life, to which he will respond one evening saying, 'I think I should move out.'

'That's a fine idea.' I concur.

Upon my return from the North West, I gift W with the ornamental sword.

"This is unlike you,' he acknowledges in the car ride back from the airport in our sporty blue jeep.
'Yes.'

I'm across the country three months later.

There is a short term of uncertainty before making a definitive decision to leave Boston.
I ask the sales help of my frequented local art store,

Pearl Paint, if they are also located in San Francisco.

'No, we're not on the West Coast.' The answer throws doubt into the trajectory.

If a sign was what I needed, however, a sign is what I got.

Handwritten in red marker, a week later, upon arriving at the art store entrance, a note on the door spells 'Moving to San Francisco.' Confused and shocked, I read and reread the print three times before comprehending. There are bags to pack.

Before I leave, W and I meet for a beer at The Bristol Café. A little treasure with warm inviting woods and music for cold northern nights. It is across the street from where we have lived for two years. We have never been in, at least not together.

I ask jokingly for a reference for the position of wife.

'You get an 'A,' he says.

This ironic comment and sentiment is unsatisfying and ultimately beguiling.

Such statements by other men will later plague me.

A familiar song keeps playing in my head as we say

goodbye in front of the apartment we once shared.

'Give me one reason to stay and I'll turn right back around. Said I don't want to leave you lonely, ya gotta make me change my mind.'

He didn't give me a reason.
I didn't turn around,
or change my mind.

) ((●)) (

When the husband moves out, it is late autumn in New England. The trees are already stark, the season of death has commenced. I sit for a while on a red chaise lounge at a friend's gallery opening, in shock from my new found freedom, then check my bank account which adds up to just enough money to purchase a big bright red vintage wool coat and a bottle of French perfume. The coat is Cadmium Red Light, and the perfume, Angel, its box, King's Blue, Rembrandt.

Angel

Top Notes: melon, coconut, mandarin orange, cassia, jasmine, bergamot, cotton candy.

Heart: honey, apricot, blackberry, plum,
orchid, peach, jasmine, lily of the
valley, rose.

Base: tonka bean, amber, patchouli, musk,
vanilla, dark chocolate, caramel.

Later I write him a poem, but as communication is not a factor in our equation, he will never see it, and it probably was never really meant for him anyway.

August

I first saw you

in overalls and shirtless, on a tractor, in the

heat of Israel's August

against the fecund northern landscape.

'I want to marry him.' I say to my sister.

After dinner, You were contrary, testing me.

But the following day, sitting by the

turquoise pool, you twist

color thread into my long hair,

then in a small bedroom your guitar playing

makes me cry.

We make love

on the bed by the large

open window.

Years later, we are in the same bed,

but you don't touch me.

You do not want me there, send me out,

then you call me back, we are here

for your dying mother.

After days with no sleep,

barely lucid,

you ask me to open the window so that yo

might 'night flight', astral travel

to the hospital room,

where you describe the ghost of your

father at the bedside of your mother.

speaking in Yiddish, and English

and languages I don't understand.

Agitated, thrashing-- I try to console you,

telling you that

angels are with you and will watch over,

a soldier, afflicted by combat, but not from

opponents.

We married a few months later,

but I think you mistook me for a spy.

Now, I am leaving through my own

open window, speaking in languages you

can't understand.

I hope the angels are still watching

over you.

I no longer can.

CHAPTER THREE

blurred edges

In classical painting class we are taught to sketch the form, filling it with light, dark, and middle tones. But I have perpetual urges to merge, to bleed and break out of limiting lines that define.

I begin to paint figures that expand beyond boundaries of human physical form and borders of skin. They emerge from the background, diffuse and blur into the surroundings, a dialogue between space and form, subject and background with textured paint and subtly changing values.

) ((●)) (

I venture out of the Prospect street apartment, embarking into the day to see what presents itself.

Seven Stars bookstore of esoterica is where I start. I scan the book spines: astrology, UFOs, tarot, shamanism. Nothing calls me.

A woman upstairs is doing channeling. I'm not sure what that is, but I have a go. I am not particularly moved or enriched by this 'channeling.'

But, as I leave the uneventful session, the channeler says, 'I'm getting a message that you should read the book, 'Hands of Light', I don't know why, I have never read it, but there you have it.'

I locate the book on a table, which, upon some thumbing through, appears to be a text book on energy healing, diagrams of astral bodies and colored auras.

I close the book and walk out- she obviously got this wrong.

My cousin, a child psychologist, connects me with a job to shadow an eight-year-old boy in a private Cam

bridge elementary school.

W has moved out. This gig should be lucrative and maybe rewarding. I meet Jared, the boy, and his mother for a preliminary interview over coffee.

He is quite a frail little thing, sleepy heavy lids, freckled chipmunk cheeks. He smiles politely, wiggling in his chair with feet dangling a foot from the floor.

I am now part of the second grade class. The children pet my burgundy velvet full bodysuit. Jared throws blocks across the class at some other children and then runs out of the building. The teacher wants Jared out altogether. His meager demeanor becomes meaner and meaner as he morphs into a petite terror.

I am given my own little office in hopes that I will occupy him for the school day and keep everyone safe.

Initially, I am told that Jared gets frustrated because he has learning challenges. Squatting on the floor of my office, he sharpens a pencil, and with great fervor, stabs my booted foot repeatedly, a maniacal grin across his face.

'How is Jared doing? Is he learning his math?' Asks his

quaffed and tailored mother, sitting in my office a few days later in all shades taupe.

'Well, when we can get past his anger.' I answer.

'He's not angry,' she replies, placing her hands in her lap.

'Actually,' I respond, 'he is REALLY angry.'

She smiles and clearing her throat explains, 'Oh no, he's just *acting* angry.'

Jared, though abusive, seems to need me. I'm the only one he has here, the only one who acknowledges that he is angry. But after years of a marriage with anger hurled in my direction at light speed, on the subway platform fresh from work, I hold back tears.

Compelled, I am back in Seven Stars bookstore purchasing the energy healing book with exact change in my pocket, eager to jump in.

I sit at my kitchen table and read. This all makes perfect sense to me. Traditional therapy only builds a road between the emotional to that of the mental. To contextualize feelings, very important, a start, but ultimately limited. I learn that there are aspects of the self that the self cannot access. This speaks to my floundering stuck state. It seems I should consult someone that has studied with the author. I successfully track down someone in the Boston area.

Perry and I meet at his office past the beautiful Mount Auburn Cemetery, with elaborate headstones and monuments. He is handsome, gracious, offering to get me a blanket if I am cold. This gesture halts me, I am not used to a man showing kindness towards me. This recognition appalls me.
I explain my situation…Jared is so angry and W was so angry …and I can't take anymore anger. They need me, but abuse the one closest.

'That's because *you* are angry.' Perry explains.

'I'm not angry.' I shuffle uneasy in an easy chair.

He smiles, 'No, you're angry.'

He asks me to recline on a massage table as he moves energy around. I actually have no idea what he is doing, but deduce this given that he is an energy healer.

A few minutes later I can neither open my eyes nor open my clenched fists.
"Open your hands." Perry directs.

'I can't.' I struggle. 'I can't.' This is very alarming from my closed eyes perspective.

He suggests that I punch the pillow to release the energy force that is paralyzing me.

'Jared is not separate from you,' he explains, 'but rather

an extension of you, and you need to see him as such, and only then, will you both heal this.'

The next morning, I take Perry's advice. Jared and I go to the gym, and at the count of three, I instruct, we will hurl ourselves into the mats that are hanging on the wall.

'One two three.' We leap into the thick foam rubber blue plastic. SMASH. A shock as our bodies hit the mats.

Release.

Laughter.

And again.

Jared's moods improve, as do mine. As he lightens, his academics, handwriting, and focus improve along with a joy of learning. They have diagnosed him all wrong. Its not his school performance that makes him upset, but rather his upset that makes it impossible for him to concentrate on school work.

We write, do math, research his favorite subject - dogs. We read about Max, a beat poet puppy and Jared writes poetry. But his parents become very concerned the day he punches a pillow.

I had brought in a pillow for him to punch as a way to

express and expel the excessive, unmet anger. And, because I am now no longer threatened by anger myself, there is no invisible cap or limit to what I can handle. He is free to fully rage, and I am comfortable letting him go as far as he needs.

His slight boy frame collapses to the ground in exhaustion. Then he crawls back up and swipes some more. And when he is done, he is done. It is done. There is peace.

The next morning we compose a poem together about the pillow which he has beaten and thrashed the day before.

The Nothing Pillow, by Jared N.

My pillow is the color of a sunset
it is soft as clouds
its nice and warm like
sitting by a warm fire in the winter,
i want to lay on my pillow,
to look at it,
and make sure its ok.
I call it the nothing pillow
because it doesn't do anything,
and when i lie on it,
i think of nothing.
the stuffing is like cotton candy,
i want to eat it.
when i hold my pillow,

I feel happy as can be,
I feel happy like a warm bed.
Good night.

His parents accuse me of riling him up.

By the end of a winter that had left Cambridge squinty bright when the sun reflected off the miles of chalky white snow, that fell that year, Jared has a new school.

A few weeks later Jared's prominent lawyer father calls to apologize for accusations and to thank me for 'keeping it together' when everyone else was 'going under.' Jared's Head of Child Psychology therapist lauds me for seeing what even he missed. He writes me a letter of recommendation for a Master's in social work at an East Coast school.

I don't get accepted. Not my destination or destiny. West coast is waiting.

) ((●)) (

I am visiting Molly at Massachusetts School of Art where she is doing her Masters in painting. We sit outside talking.

'A girl in my class is going to be on Oprah tomorrow.' Molly reports.

'Oh, yeah, for what?' I sip some coffee from the school cafeteria.

'She says she's been abducted by aliens.'

I let out one of my infamously loud laughs, detectable in crowded movie theaters and commented on frequently for its robust and subterranean quality.

'She is really serious about this, it's a big deal to her.' I'm politely scolded. I apologize for my insensitivity and turn on Oprah the next afternoon out of curiosity and because I am home.

The first guest to come out on stage with Oprah is none other than energy healer Perry. My healer Perry!

He sits across from Oprah talking about alien abduction, his abductions, with background footage of him and his wife boating and him walking along the Charles River.

I flip.

The bubble called reality has gone pop.
I just mutter, 'Me, Perry, Oprah, aliens… pointing to Perry, sitting next to Oprah on the couch and then I point in the air upward referring to aliens. I repeat this several times trying to connect the dots, the dots have taken me right off the page.

'Me, Perry, Oprah, aliens....me, Perry, Oprah, Aliens.... me, Perry, Oprah, aliens.' One degree of separation from Oprah, one degree from the aliens!

) ((●)) (

I make enough money from the Jared job to move to Berkley.

Before I leave I introduce my German artist friend Deirdre, who has had her own encounters with aliens, to Perry. But, she and I will terminate our friendship when I point out to her that she treats me like 'the ugly friend', a term used in Hollywood casting to make the lead more attractive, the bridesmaid dress principle.

I will see both Perry and Deirdre in a documentary about abductions years later. Along with John Mack, a Harvard professor and Pulitzer Prize winner, who will be suspiciously killed when struck by a car in London. Perry explains that it had been years since his last abduction and although the abductions were physically painful, he was missing being 'chosen' and now feels forsaken. I am moved by this.

Somehow I understand.

) ((●)) (

Preparing for a solitary year in Berkeley, I designate this time to write since I won't have access to a painting studio. But, this is not how it goes.

Within a matter of weeks, I am successfully integrated and acclimated into my new setting. There is the ritual shopping at Berkeley Bowl, where I seem quite habituated running into friends in every aisle- old friends from back East who hook me up with work, new friends from work who hook me up with parties, parties where everyone 'hooks up.'

) ((●)) (

It is still curious how we three become so interwoven, Amil, Gustav, and I, who first meet at the Med, yet it isn't long before our unlikely trio begins to refer to ourselves as 'the organism', conjuring an image of an

amorphous mass wiggling restlessly, aimlessly, by ome biological imperative.

I call them the Gemini boys, born at the end of May, only a few days apart. They are also quite intelligent, and attractive, adding to their severe sense of entitlement. Both enjoy coffee at the Med, but their similarities end there.

By all accounts, Amil is ethically challenged - recently romantically rejected, severely intoxicated, an all around brat who enjoys death defying recreation like base jumping. Gus, conversely, prefers watching The Simpsons stoned, safely sitting on his plush mossy green couch drinking port, or drinking beer at a really dark dance club.

We drink recklessly till dawn during nights at Amil's apartment, Kettle One, or two or three. Roommates regularly scramble to wake him at four am to get him to San Francisco stock exchange where he makes ample cash to satiate himself and indulge the organism with the Bay Areas finest food and drink.

While at a college bar on Shattuck Avenue, one night, Amil expresses a wish to paint and I agree to teach him. In return, he offers to provide art supplies. He will rent us a studio.

I'm back.

) ((●)) (

Extras at the cafe-

A refugee from the eighties rock scene, with long thin dyed dried black hair against pale skin, silver rings on his fingers. His rotting teeth are exposed by his ever kind smile and nature.

A bald ex-military fellow, a little slow because of a head injury in combat, exacerbated by a subsequent motorcycle collision- a childlike simplicity, and fascination with snakes, which I enjoy holding when he brings them to the cafe.

A blond woman who dresses like a Hara Krishna and moves mysteriously about the neighborhood and has a surprising and brief relationship with the rocker.

A roofer, with muscular physique, always hiding his vulnerability and stoner eyes behind dark glasses. He gets the attractive sales woman at the boutique next door pregnant, they marry.

A middle-aged stocky Scorpion ex porn star who is a recovering addict, single parent, with colorful tattoos covering his arms. He has a jovial warm greeting and a handlebar mustache.

His buddy, a hyper speed addict, tight jeans, infectious grin, always in some trouble, dancing the tango with things that provoke suspicion.

And a blues musician in his late sixty's, with some notoriety in his youth, humble and generous, with kind words for everyone.

The floors in the two story Mediterranean Cafe, known by all as 'the Med', are black and white tiled, the bathrooms are graffiti.

Towards the end of one of my favorite films, The Graduate, Dustin Hoffman, a forlorn Benjamin in pursuit of Elaine, sits desperately at this very window seat at the 'Med' facing Mo's book store across the street. This confirms my providential connection with the Café, with Hoffman or with the infelicitous, and awkward nature of love.

There are regulars who partake in the day shift, those like my house-mate, Susan, who meets her cronies, balding men and rounding long gray haired women, all in bright tie-dye shirts, for a late afternoon banter on politics and art.

The cafe street tables are home to the nocturnal crew who wear darker shades, black and red, black and denim, black and black, as do I, though I will make concerted efforts to introduce a bit of pink or teal or amber in the way of a silk scarf.

The poet Yehudah Amichai comes to speak at the Berkeley Campus, my first fall there. I sketch him while he reads from the podium.
In the middle of this century we turned to each other. I saw your body, casting the shadow, waiting for me. The leather straps of a long journey had long since been tightened crisscross on my chest. I spoke in praise of your mortal loins, you spoke in praise of my transient face, I stroked your hair in the direction of your journey, I touched the tidings of your last day, I touched your hand that has never slept, I touched your mouth that now, perhaps, will sing.

The next day I get the flu and am sick all winter. By spring, I'm diagnosed with walking pneumonia. According to Louise Haye, this lung infection is a result of depression, grief or fear of life or not feeling worthy.

If this is the case, the horrible late night coughing fits and bouts of fever certainly slow down the folly of a new town and life, making me take time to mend.

In the years that will follow, from time to time, I am stricken with inexplicable coughing spells that last weeks and force me to sleep with throat lozenges by my bed.
Still more healing is needed, more life to take in.

) ((●)) (

My bedroom, in a craftsman house, has huge leafy plants outside the window that resemble what one might expect to find on another planet. An old lemon tree in the small backyard has over ripe lemons the size of grapefruits, that 'PLOP' to the ground in citrus explosion. Most importantly, however, the house is only 0.6 miles to 'the Med.'

In my small room, I sketch with charcoal.

During that summer, the North Berkeley Montessori Elementary School where I teach art, hires me to do a theater workshop with the younger children.

I choose to dramatize an old favorite Yiddish story from childhood, a story I had first heard from my father which goes like this:

'There was righteous man, Reb Itzik Feivel, who night after night had the same dream. The dream urged him to travel to the City of Prague and there, beneath the Royal bridge along the Vlotslov River, he should dig, for a great treasure awaited him.

He traveled for quite some time from his home in Krakow and when he arrived there, he found soldiers guarding the bridge day and night.

When he began to dig, the guard approached him and inquired, ' old man, what are you doing here digging ?'
The man, holding a small shovel explained that he had reoccurring dreams which has led him to search for his treasure.

'Ha!' the soldier scoffed. 'I too, have a reoccurring dream. I dream that in the town of Krakow there's a man named Rabbi Itzik Feival, the son of Rabbi Yekalis, and that there's a huge treasure buried under the pot belly stove in his home. Do you see me running off to Krakow? Only a fool chases after the messages in a dream.'

Immediately the modest Reb Itzik understood that he had to come to Prague to receive the rest of the message that came through the soldier.

'Yes, yes,' he answered. I will take your advice and go home now.'

He went back home, dug underneath his stove and sure enough there he found a great fortune of gold and jewels.

Rabbi Itzik thus became very wealthy and gave a large amount of his riches to the poor, becoming a hero to those in his humble community.'

Though, for that short time, I had entertained the idea of moving to Prague for reasons unclear, the play was not going well. Perhaps it was the wrong story. I would certainly realize later that despite breathtaking architecture, I would be wrong about wanting to move there.

My eyes are on the ground as I walk down Telegraph Avenue that sunlit July morning, thinking of how to fix the play, when I spot and pick up a card lying on the street. It's an old Tarot card, the Four of Wands, and if recollection serves, this is not a favorable card.

~Mental Exhaustion, Stress,
Overwhelmed, Retreat~

A divination dilemma. Now that I have picked up this card, what is the proper esoteric etiquette? Can I simply leave it where I found it? Is this in poor occult form? Am I stuck with this future, or can it be changed? How does this work?

I make my way down the avenue, staring at its intricate design, contemplating free will and fate. When I look up a few blocks down, I see a sign, 'Tarot Readings here.'

Yes...hmm...consult an expert, I think, as I approach the reader, a young man dressed in a red velvet frock coat, a dandy feathered hat and renaissance fair boots.

'You just found this card?' he repeats slowly, urging me to reveal every detail of the occurrence.

'Yeah, just now on the street.' For illustrative effect, I point back up Telegraph.

'So, can I pull a new card?' I ask, eager to remedy my ill fate and get to work on time.

'I'll tell you what,' says the Tarot reader, with sinister good looks, 'I'll let you pull a card if you give me this Four of Swords.'

'Agreed.' A deal is struck.

As I procedurally shuffle the deck, we sit down in his make shift tent. He proceeds to tell a story. Years ago he had a very unique deck that was very special to him. He traveled quite a bit and during that time, and had lost a card from this very deck that he kept in a duffle bag with all his other possessions.

And curiously, this card that I had found is the exact one missing from his beloved deck.
I pull a new card. Six of Wands. Victory!
Six of wands: The main focus of this card is on success and winning. When you see this card, you know that it is time you receive some well deserved praise for your hard work. This praise, while it can be public, can also be a private thing. Self-praise is just as important as

praise from others. Another big factor of this card is acknowledgment – being able to recognize your own successes and the successes of others.
As per agreement, I gift him the Four of Swords, having reversed my fate.

A transformation transaction.

His deck is now complete and I have a new outcome to the play about needing to engage a stranger who holds a piece of your fortune.

I continue across the green Berkeley campus. My decision to tell this story is affirmed as I seem to have just lived its message. I suspect that not all exchanges appear as victory, but they just might be all the same.

I never do move to Prague, home of the mystic Ma'haral and his legendary Golam, the inspiration for Shelly's Frankenstein. But, I do chaperone a trip for teenagers there one summer, and while training to tour guide the teens, I am given the afternoon off to enjoy a perfect espresso in a medieval cafe under the Vltava River on my birthday.

I am very concerned, however, that I will not remember the many dates and facts to properly relay the story of Kafka's life, the subjects of the tour. The next day, I sit at Kafka's café hoping that by osmosis, I will somehow come to know him. When I learn that his birthday, like Herman Hesse, is the same week as mine, I can put his entire life in this new lens. Sharing the same astrological sign, along with Marcel Proust, I know he must be deeply sensitive. This surprises me as I imagined he had more of an air like nature, like Aquarius. Knowing that he is a water sign changes everything. I had him all wrong.

This awareness initiates me as a tour guide through this wondrous Gothic city.

I clear out the old garage, turning it into a studio in the backyard of Susan's home. Although I am proud of my gumption and the freshly painted turquoise cement floor, the leaking roof renders the space more or less nonfunctional, particularly more so during Berkeley rainy season.

So, I flee to the Med Cafe for coffee to warm up the damp in my bones, and seek out art and poetry books at Moe's on Telegraph with Amil.

On dry days, I sketch myself with oil pastels in a rust color flower print dress, hair a poof, and teach Amil how to paint.

He will later become both a fine human and designer and mentions me affectionately in a Ted talk.

"It's so hard," he whines, bottle of Vodka resting precariously on the glass palette.

'This is not about posing as an artist to pick up girls,' I bristle, 'This is the real deal. This is art. It's hard. Real artists are working, not hanging out at clubs trying to impress each other, boasting that they're artists. They are too busy!' My voice sharpens with each point, the crease in my forehead deepens.

His lean body shudders and he sulks with a cigarette and a whimper, while I settle into nominal satisfaction for having defended the honor of my centuries old craft.

We go on field trips for art supplies in SF's Pearl Art and Crafts. I take a moment to appreciate the synchronicity of the store's move out west and the divine hand in their hand written sign.

Amil rents a live in art studio where I sleep a few nights a week.

He goes off to work at the stock exchange at four a.m. and when I wake many hours later, I make French Roast in a press, the only 'food' in the white walled studio.

Eating out together on Telegraph is the routine when Amil comes home, and sometimes the weekly poetry readings in Oakland.

At the Med Cafe, I scribble a poem on a yellow legal pad a poem that I will not perform publicly.

My eyes, usually
Green are wide
Open, nearly black
With pupils
Expanded,
Adjusting to the
Nightness that
Surrounds and
Holds us
In a bed
That tempts
Touch.

But you sleep
Your breath
Is on my back
then we roll
over,
and my fingers like
trespassers
trace the routs
of your muscle
and bone
as I consider
the things forbidden
between
Platonics.

In the dark,
Shapes blur.

We become one
Without distinction
Between the tones of
Our flesh,
The positions of parts.

At night
We are artists, by night,
My paintings
Wait for me
In the corner.
While you write
And quilt music.

But light demands
That we distill this
Space
Between,
Define the edges,
Create boundaries,
Like church stain glass
Windows,
Distinguishing

My round forms
In Semitic hues
From you,
Angular

Warm and dark,
That I would mix
With ochres and cadmiums

Because with the sun
You rise
As market maker
Risk manager,
Analytical, critical,
Minimizing risk,
Avoiding
Loss.
In the morning,
I am still an artist.
Playing with negative
And positive shapes.
Dancing in the tension
Between.
Still the child
Desiring
To color
Out of the lines.

CHAPTER FOUR

total eclipse

During a bi-coastal conversation with a bi-racial friend, one time studio and roommate, and occasional lover over many years, LJ, states that he could never be with me because I am white and could therefore, never really understand him.

'You are too Jewish,' he points out, and too white apparently, and I suspect that I am just too much me.

Years later I presume that he is too-misogynistic, anti-Semitic, divisive, fearful.

My paintings express my urges to merge beyond flesh - skin is but a well tailored suit, a costume specifying color, race and sex.

I am cast in the role of woman, female, I am given this

part to play. It comes with some character subtext-mine is quirky and sometimes intense.

Occasionally, I appeal to the director to change some minor details. But I try not to forget that this is a role and that we just have parts to play. I try to play mine well, but its tricky. I really have no idea how to do this. And, where shall I look for role models to research. This part offers the opportunity for humility. Lots of humility.

This, I have down.

I roll up a single black stocking and place it with a note next to his computer, that reads, 'redeemable for the pair.' How much do I play into eroticism, dress up to un-dress?

I don't like games as a child. The one's I did play, I played by my own rules. 'Board' games describe how I felt.

One board game we had at home was Masterpiece, the goal, to match a painting with a price tag. The one who acquired the million-dollar painting was the winner.

I aimed rather, to get the white Georgia O'Keeffe, 'Cow's Skull with Calico Roses,' 1931. My favorite painting. And then I win.

People said of O'Keeffe's work, 'flowers that look like vulvas!' Of my work, they say, 'So, O'Keeffe, but vulvas that look like flowers!'

Some people see life like a game and play it as such.

If I have to play a game, I have already lost, because I don't want to be playing. Games make me sad.

And boy girl games of seduction confuse.

And very few seem to play them well.

Women stomp like sumo wrestlers in sought after clothes and heels, handbags and jewelry, with no elegance of movement, no elegance of language or of thought.
Shaving and sheered like sheep, in thongs, the female follows trends mindlessly.

With equal attention to heart, mind and soul, I can give my body in the visual costumes that please - like occasional high heel that, by forcing the back to arch, pushes the bust forward and butt backwards, accentuating feminine contours making legs look longer and slender and toned. So I have read.

A romantic involvement that allows for honest sharing of pleasure and preference can be evocative, provocative, amative. Intimate.

My biggest erogenous zone is my heart.

My G spot stands for Grace, I tell him.

In a book of the San Francisco Ballet there is a photo of a dancer leaping or flying. This is Ikolo. I meet him at a small party in the Mission. He is half Jewish and half African American. He tells me that his Swahili name means 'the loudest drum.' He wants a Hebrew name too. I create one for him by changing one letter- *Elkolo*, God is his voice.

He examines my foot.

“See, my foot is superior to yours” says Ikolo, showing me the extreme arch of his ballet dancer’s foot.
“My feet are actually perfect for another type of dance,” I explain.

I’m not sure which, maybe it’s Leonard Cohen’s ‘Dance to the End of Love.’

He concedes.

In the same ballet book, a costume designer is asked, ‘Why do you spend so much time on the costume details if the audience will never see it?

‘The dancers will see it and will dance better because of it.’ She answers.

I am wearing a black tunic from a thrift store in little India, embroidered with pink and white flowers and pale green accent. Today I will write better because of it. I will use my female sensual sensibilities and not fight or deny them as I might have before. Nor will I use them as an excuse.

Female artists have had a rough go at it.

When I meet Ikolo, I’m not sure if I should tell him that I hated the ballet he was in, that I had reacted to it like Poison Ivy and had sketched all through it to avoid watching the stage. Because these patrons of the arts, filling the rows, clapping respectfully, believe they are being filled with culture's choice cuts. Something is wrong. I can sense Balanchine's misogyny. I can feel what he has done to the women under his scrutiny. I feel the oppression of women ballet dancers, the dismissal of those who no longer keep his interest. The prized prima ballerina, tea cup feet bound in wood and pink silk.

It is at a performance by the San Francisco ballet that I experience a bizarre reaction to public art that I will call, in jest, CCSS, Collective Conscience Sensitivity Syndrome. I seem to be particularly effected by art as experienced by a large group, somehow intensified and magnified.

Three other times I recall this adverse reaction.

A New England rock concert, drunk fans screaming and shouting, as the singer sings a confessional song,

'I'm digging in the dirt
Stay with me I need support
I'm digging in the dirt
To find the places I got hurt
To open up the places I got hurt.'

A Tantric Puja.
And also, at the San Francisco Museum of Art. An exhibit of 20th century woman artists as Sunday brunching culture vultures peruse the gallery scene, non-

chalantly passing the blood art of woman who suffer immeasurably for their art to hang, nailed to the wall.

'Do you know? Do you know how they suffered?' I am pained by or for the work, as if the art itself is alive. Maybe it is. I am personally assaulted, the sting of salt. Swallowed by sorrow. There is not enough air, the space seems compressed, yellowing dim, stale.

) ((●)) (

'It is not easy to be a young artist,' remarked surrealist Meret Oppenheim, 'and more difficult to be a *woman* artist.'

After leaving Paris in 1939, prior to the outbreak of World War ll, suffering from the rejection and condescending culture of her male peers, Oppenheim said, 'A millennia of discrimination against women was resting on my shoulders... embodied in my feelings of inferiority.'

Frieda Kahlo, her uterus impaled in a trolley car accident, had a tumultuous marriage with Diego Rivera, as well as multiple surgeries, infidelities, and miscarriages.

'I hope the exit is joyful - and I hope never to return.' says Frieda.

Eva Hesse, born into the upheaval and persecution of a Jewish family in Nazi Germany, later flees to New York, where her mother kills herself. After Eva's own failed marriage, she nonetheless rises to stardom in the New York's art scene of the sixties. But at age thirty four, the Yale graduate will succumb to a brain tumor that kills her all the same.

And Francesca Woodman, a photographer, who I come across that day at the museum. I fall in love with a self-portrait, a black and white of intimate, ethereal lights contrasting against shades of pitch and charcoal. Are these the kind of photos Marthe would take if she had been born one hundred years later, and had her own career? Woodman was both photographer and model.

I have an immediate, thorough and profound affinity to Francesca's work. Her black and white images touch a deep and essential aspect of myself like no other. She is posing in feminine and traditional white Victorian slips against a rustic and raw studio. She creates her images looking into reflective surfaces, but never directly, hiding and exposing, present yet fleeting, contemporary and timeless.
Here and not.

The title card next to her work notes that Woodman killed herself at age twenty-two.

) ((●)) (

One day during the late winter torrential rains in Los Angeles, the kind that cause mudslides and road closings in the Canyon, an older woman with warm grandmother like complexion and white hair, sits at a table behind me at the cafe crying. I engage the woman with British accent who explains that all of her belongings are ruined, her bedding soaked.

It becomes clear that she is among the many homeless in the neighborhood. It continues to pour. I buy her a pot of tea something to eat and run home, just a few blocks, to find her some dry cloths and a dry blanket. Her name is Sonya.

During a police sweep of the homeless in the neighborhood some weeks later, a panicked Sonya is knocking on my door hoping to stay the night and avoid being arrested. The night becomes a week becomes a month and for the month of March, Sonya camps on my couch.

I try to find her work, get her situated as a live in caretaker, but slowly come to learn that every homeless person has their own reasons for their situation, and that the homeless issue is not an easy solve and some don't want to be 'solved' and some don't want to be easy.

One of these evenings early spring, on my way home down the back alley, I find two bags of women's clothes that someone has left for the taking.

I bring the treasure home and Sonya and I celebrate the windfall trying on clothes, giggling like schoolgirls, splitting up the booty.

That night, I lay awake experiencing something unfamiliar, trying to detect this unusual feeling? I couldn't quite locate this emotion… Aha! The absence of loneliness. I lay there enjoying this strange and delightful sensation, the simple company of my fellow human being.

In high school, I develop an inexplicable fear of being committed to a mental institution. Friends joke all the time, 'M, your crazy!' but it's never funny to me, on the contrary.
I am very concerned.

I know without doubt, that I am the opposite of crazy- deep and clear like Mediterranean Sea, but I am beginning to understand the narrow scope of human comfort, of what people allow, tolerate, expect, and prefer. Parameters constrict. Asserting or declaring one's individuality is now only a matter of choosing between orange or green newest model cell phone, or i-something.

My teenage self needs answers. Who decides who is insane? I need information. I need to protect myself, because I do not fit into these narrow margins and I'm not sure how much I want to, how much I am able.

Not until I take a class in college, 'Madness in Film', will I see my fears realized on the huge lecture hall screen. And then over and over again, more films confirm the history of institutionalizing creative women. I'm even more anguished.

I soon discover Camille Claudel, renowned sculptor. Rodin's student, model, collaborator and lover, who was said to have been more talented than he, sculpting in marble the more difficult hands and feet of his sculptures.

Janet Frame, a New Zealand writer, who's story is told by filmmaker Jane Campion in *An Angel at my Table* is institutionalized after being misdiagnosed as a schizophrenic. She narrowly escapes a lobotomy.

Oy vaysmere, would exclaim, my Bubbe, Gert, with heavy Yiddish accent.

Seraphine de Senlis, dies in a French mental institution in 1942, just one year before Camille dies. Today, her decorative floral paintings hang in many museums.

Like the echoing wails of mental patients that I can

hear out the windows of the brick walled building of the state psychiatric hospital, where my father works as a chaplain and brings us to help out during their holidays celebrations.

I am a young girl when a raspy voiced woman with grey hair at the hospital, clutching a black patent-leather purse says that her dead baby is inside it.

My gut tightens. My throat clamps. My eyes fix on the shiny coffin shaped purse, could this be true?

I am distraught.

The emotional rip tides when engaging in art make me consider the pillaged lineage of those before me.

Terror still lurks and surfaces.

What to make of this?

Is it male fear and hate of the wild and deep thalassic, female nature, or do women hurl themselves too close to the flame?

I think of my male counterparts and their ability to compartmentalize. I thought this was lack of care, insensitivity. Defiance. Because, as much as they access real and raw emotion, they seem to have the ability to put down the pen, close the computer, clean the brushes and walk away.

My sex seems less inclined in these ways.

Whereas men can make a fire on the grill, prepare the steak dinner and enjoy the meal, women set the house ablaze, sit in the ashes, shocked and amazed by the inferno of billowing crimson and orange- total destruction.

Are we like Joan of Arc, a phoenix, unafraid of flames, knowing we will rise again winged? Or is the pain of the alternatives so great that we surrender to it, preferring to burn than to forebear?

I run this past Finn. 'Men are built for self preservation.' He agrees.
Women allow for total eclipse, more concerned with the preservation of the other. And art is 'other.'

Total eclipse. Total *karban*, the Hebrew word for sacrifice. Crawling onto the alter of our own making.

And what of the women writers?

Anne Sexton
Sylvia Plath
Dorothy Parker
Virginia Wolf

Political graphic novelist, JD, and I discuss this during a writing break at the cafe.

'It's hard to know what is 'outside' the patriarchal construction, separate from gender... correctly sort out cognition... maybe art is like sex in this regard.' He says, 'Guys are visual, women are experiential- men want to see and appreciate the experience, woman want the transcendental, the meaningful.'
'Yes!' I respond, having always felt that art comes from the same place, wanting to fully fuse with my man or my art- a propensity to burn for both. No half measures. Unable to disconnect.

Perhaps this is the evolutionary leap necessary for the survival of my species- passion without persecution, making art from a place of virtue, not a predominating emotion.

Instead of creating from rage, sorrow and indulgent states, create from beauty, truth, courage!
Because the energy is carried in to the work, and from it emanates.

) ((●)) (

On one day of the year, the high priest of the Children of Israel would enter the Holy of Holies, the inner sanctum of the great Temple in Jerusalem. Folklore tells that a gold chord was tied around the High Priest's leg, for only one deserving of the honor to represent the people in beseeching God could safely carry out this task. If undeserving and lacking in righteousness, his lifeless body would have to be pulled out.

The act of creating art elicits this scenario. The fear that I might not return from the inner sanctum- an astronaut weightless spinning in space. Ground Control to Major Tom, life sustaining umbilical chord, severed.

Finn sits at the cafe to my left, or sometimes to the right, back or in front of me - like Archangels in all directions, composing music or editing film, while I write. In this confluence of cause and effect, comfort and umbrage, a muse.

I want to believe it is so, that he has my back, that I may bravely go enter the holy of holies, or out into the sea, to return with treasures, if only a pearl.

'Yes, you can do it! Just keep letting the thoughts come through.' He emails me, hearing me sigh and watching me struggle with the birthing process.
But, he tells me he doesn't want my back, or any part of me to sit close to him while he works, creating any acknowledgment of a connection between us.

Well I said, 'Lily, oh Lily I don't feel safe I feel that life has blown a great big hole through me' And she said 'Child, you must protect yourself, You can protect yourself I'll show you how with fire'. Gabriel before me Raphael behind me Michael to my right Uriel on my left side In the circle of fire.

~ Kate Bush

Either way. I'm going in.
And I do. And inside I wrestle with versions of real, the true color of things, that I might emerge with a story to tell myself, to tell him, or anyone who will listen.

But, like Monet's Rouen Cathedral paintings, dependent on the time of day, the whether or season, the church facade can appear as pink or blue, in gold or grays. Truth comes in a varied palette.

) ((●)) (

Maybe I am periwinkle, a violet blue, Jacaranda blossoms in spring, properties of both warm and cool- silvery elusive moon, or warm violet.
Perhaps Finn is burgundy. Cabernet sauvignon, Redwood for building a boat or the well varnished bar in a cozy pub- color of strength, dignity, and the wool sweater I will give him.

Together we make the Vesper.
The darkening sky, preparing for its celestial pageantry.
Portal into night.
Or the color of the first lights of day, primordial hope where optimism is born from darkness.

Or, maybe he is eternal electric indigo, or stingray metallic, like the mineral osmiridium, used for tips of pen nibs, surgical needles, and sparking points in engines, or, lion's mane gold.

Perhaps I am dank forest moss. Or ocean mist.

Really, we too are the cathedrals, changing from one moment to the next - opportunity to express and create infinite combinations, prisms of possibility.
These are only the romantic tendencies of a periwinkle poet, because with every flush and flutter, I will be reminded to adjust my eyesight, afflicted by the condition of rose-colored retinas.

To him, I can feel like a full service filling station and he does not care what color.

'I want truth.' I tell him, aware of my predilection to colorize, enhance the image, the painter or director's privilege and prerogative in creating.

So, like a homeopathic remedy, Finn is the poison that helps strengthen the immune system, the principle of anti venom, where poison is injected into the system to initiate an immune system response.

Antivenomous serotherapy was first developed in 1895 by French physician Albert Calmette, who, interestingly, was born a year after Debussy and a year before Camille.

Finn is my homeopathic remedy, the master story teller that induces the elements to create a new narrative. I need a new story. So, I write-care-ful not to get stuck writing the old story, another trick of demons, dressed as a muse.

But, I suspect that in reality, I need to be free of a story altogether, a writer without a story, yes, then *everyone's* story and *no ones story* will be mine.

Outside, Finn hand rolls a cigarette.

'I'm sorry, I know I'm not easy.'

'What about me goes for easy?' I point out, 'I make art not because it's easy, but I pick projects that are worth the sacrifice, because they are valuable. You are valuable, you are worth it.'

He says that his shattered shards will aggravate and inflame me.

He preserves.
I burn like temple frankincense.

) ((●)) (

Midrash: a biblical literary art form of filling in the blanks. An artifice I too employ.

Midrash 1:
I am Camille Claudel, or her aborted child from Rodin, in limbo- floating, a ghost, watching, wanting, waiting. Bitterness from disappointment must never become

more powerful than the ability to transcend it.

I see so many women, by midlife, overcome by anger for the life that they feel is not theirs- for their unborn children, or the children they must raise alone, and the sacrifices. Bitterness gets into the veins, constricting the heart, inflaming the mind.

I proscribe Aurum Metallicum, a Homeopathic rem

edy for my ghosts and the ghosts of Renee Monchaty and L'wren, for feelings of self-condemnation, worthlessness, despondency and thoughts of suicide triggered by relationship break-ups or business failures, as joy for life is eclipsed with only feelings of despair.

L'wren Scott, had poison in her veins, weakening her, clogging arteries of invention, vessels of intention. Another model and artist, another suicide. Designer L'wren needs to go home too. She never made it to her jubilee birthday.

I come into her story, or she into mine, as we are linked by one degree of separation.

There is a small boy in my class, his mommy has just died of cancer leaving him and two younger siblings. He is sad and stoic and when we sit on the floor reading aloud from a picture book, he inches close to me and climbs into my lap.

His father then meets a beautiful women who falls in love with the family, and they with her. She is friends with L'wren Scott who designs her wedding dress. Photos appear in magazines. One photo stands out: L'wren in an elegant vintage dress, next to the bride. All else bleaches into radiant light, but L'wren, a lithe silhouette in black, like a onyx statue from an English garden, Parisian palace, or Italian courtyard, fountain or piazza.

Before turning 50, L'wren sits at the center of her web, feeling into the emptiness of the things she could not hold onto, or control. A failing career, the infidelities of the love of her life, the choices, the sacrifices that neutered dreams of having her own children.

I share none of her triumphs and every one of her defeats.

) ((●)) (

Five women: Artists, models, lovers.
One wife, one mother, two suicides.

Rose Beuret is Rodin's faithful model, mistress, housekeeper and mother of his child. Having grown up together, she supports him as he begins his career. Rose accepts, it seems, his love and affection for Camille.

I map out a time line. A lifeline.
Camille Claudel- in many ways is Rodin's partner, his equal, perhaps even more talented than he, but she falls into despair and, it seems, eventual madness because he will not leave Rose.

Marthe de Méligny is with Pierre Bonnard for years before they marry in 1925. She endures his infidelities with Renée Monchaty- Pierre's model for a brief period, dismissed around the time of Marthe and Pier's marriage.

Renee takes her own life when her love and services are terminated by Pierre. Decades later, a play is produced about her entitled 'The Human Fruit Bowl.' Rumor held that she was found dead in the bathtub. A location heavily featured in Bonnard's work.

Did they all know each other socially, meeting at the famed Parisian parties of the 20's? Do they nod at dinner after concerts or art exhibitions at Gare de Lyon or La Train Bleu, where L'wren would later meet Mick Jagger. Do they pass each other at the market, buying art supplies, a bottle of wine, a wedge of cheese?

Camille was born in 1864 and Marthe in the following year, Bonnard, in 1867 and Rodin, their senior, born in 1840.

Debussy, two years older than Camille, meets her in 1889.

Camille gives Debussy a small sculpture of two nude figures, passionately embracing, as they are swept up in the movement and drapery of *The Waltz.* He keeps it on his piano till his death in 1918.

Debussy rewrites his composition of *Clair de Lune* the next year.

Rodin dislikes Debussy's music.

Camille dares to have love and art with the man who is both to her.

Rodin refuses to leave Rose and Camille loses everything. She lives out her life, thirty years, in an insane asylum - one of the most beautiful and promising talents of the 20th century.

It is reported that every time Rodin saw one of Camille's sculptures, he succumb to inconsolable weeping.

She burns like wild fire, until they lock her up.
Then she burns silently, smoldering glowing embers.

I'm gathering ghosts.
I am building ladders to lead the ghosts home.

On a rainy ides of March, I want to collapse. How do I do it, rectify all that is shattered? How do I survive my own grief while bringing theirs to the light? How do I keep my fingers typing on these black illuminated keys and how would I paint the color gray that frames Finn I see outside the cafe window, gray but full of light? A gray that will give way to a downpour.

LJ and I struggle to plan our first outing, a lunch date at the pizza parlor across the street from the school of Fine Arts. We are now both seniors. It's hard to find common ground- I prefer the dark edgy clubs like The

Rat, a bar with beer and cigarette ash soaked carpets. He frequents the sports bars. Pizza is safe, neutral territory, with myself in a vintage black slip and he in an oxford shirt, we can unobtrusively coexist.

But this day, I am tired of words. I tell him that I cannot speak anymore, he says that is fine. We eat lunch in silence, and he is endeared to me.

Years later, after he moves out of state, he visits me in Boston. We stay up all night painting in my studio, fully stocked with Dunkin' Donuts coffee from across the street, and wine. We sleep on a mattress on the floor at dawn.

He says that any women that can top this, he will marry.

No one does.

And he never did.

And I write.
Maybe this is how I build shelving. Compartments for things.

Com- a -part - mental- ize. I write a short story:

A Place To Put

Once upon a time there was a woman. She was

an art making, color dancing, searching, soul woman.

On her path she met an art making man, he was a freedom thriving, monk of a man.

Once in the spring, the woman exhausted by words, felt she could talk no longer, so they eat lunch in silence, only smiling at each other from across the table, they became deep spirit friends, who over many years shared much of themselves. They had shared, ideas, studios, ponderings and sometimes bodies and energy.
Seeing what he needed, the woman gave him canvas and tubes of paint and said 'bring yourself out- go create'. The man took the gift and went away for a long while.

She felt sad when he was away, for although their paths seemed to take them to opposite destinations (and opposites are mirror images of the same thing), it was the miles of mindage which created real distance.

The woman missed him as if part of herself was quieted, for he was like her inner dialogue.

When he returned, he presented her with a gift of a painting, which was as large as it was beautiful- radiating color and truth.

My house, though lovely, is humble and not quite so spacious. There are no walls large enough to accommodate such a painting, the woman admitted mournfully. The man looked disappointed.

'Then build a new house.' He concluded, an obvious solution.

The woman considered what would need to get rearranged, reorganized, reconstructed, in order to accept the gift. She was not convinced that moving was right for her, and she did not yet have tools to build anew.

She struggled with her options.

'Maybe I could cut the painting into smaller pieces? Yet something so whole and so perfect could not survive being quartered without destroying its intent, integrity, and intensity' she thought on.

'Copy and reduce it?' But she quickly realized that this would diminish its texture, definition and luminosity. This would not do either.

The woman wrestled some more, 'Can I accept this gift without sacrifice? Is it possible to honor this gift, and its giver, as well as myself? The woman knew that to deny this painting is to deny beauty and love and light, though light can blind and blindness is a darkness which too can bring illumination. This is an offering from one who has traveled deep and far to bring this back. Is rejecting the gift rejecting life itself?

'Perhaps I can keep this painting if you come here and build a house with me' suggested the woman, unsure herself if this in fact was a perfect plan.

'No. I have to stay here and make my paintings.' Said the man.

'Yes.' Acknowledged the woman.

Soon the dark purple struggle became iridescent pinks and shimmering minnow fish blue as the woman understood what to do.

My home is here and I will stay as long as it suits me. There may be a splendid palace in my future, or maybe a mere sanctuary will suffice, but I gratefully accept your gift and will treasure it always.

I will make it a blanket that spreads out over my

bed, warming, shielding and comforting me at night like a canopy of jeweled color. I will lay beneath it in priestly solitude or entwined with my lover, basking in light, creating light, and dreaming.'

My life has become creating Places to Put.

CHAPTER FIVE

weight of light

(fools, ghosts, witches and angels)

LJ is the collaboration of a white sculptor mother and black painter father. They sculpted a son and painted him bronze. But he never feels right in his swarthy skin and believes that women and wives ruin a male artist's life, as his mom did to his dad.

When my brother dies of a brain tumor, LJ comes to the funeral. He wears a gray cap. Years pass and he too gets a brain tumor.

When LJ's tumor is removed, so are his many demons and it is like a new birthday, a day that starts off with a brilliant sunrise. LJ apologizes for his hurtful behavior over the years and I accept because I have long forgiven him- he gave me a little blue book that would loom large later.

) ((●)) (

Screenplay:
Weight of Light

The phone rings.
She answers the phone.
Her expression changes, sober.

EXT. LAX. LOS ANGELES AIRPORT, NIGHT

MUSIC: Jenny Dalton, 'Snow Mazes of Norway.'

Image of an airplane taking off, the sound of the jet engine.

INT. HOSPICE ROOM. DAY

View outside of the window snow on the ground and icy branches.

Ani is with her family members gathered around the bed of her younger brother who is dying. The mood is somber.

She looks around his bedroom at his

hat rack with an extensive hat collection

including a Russian fur trimmed hat, baseball caps, a Persian FEZ, an old fashioned bowler. She eyes a photo of him with sports notables.
Ani is standing at the foot of his bed as he gasps for his last breath.

She has that distinct look of one who has witnessed the shallow veil between life and death- the soul's mysterious transition of departure.

ANI
(whispers to herself)
Where did you go?
(an echo in her thoughts)
Where did you go?

INT. CHAPEL. DAY

The casket is front and center. Ani is in the first row with her family.
She is wearing one of his eccentric hats from his collection. Her siblings look rather conservatively dressed in comparison.

During my second semester of Rabbinical school I get a call from my mother. I would need to come home right away if I want to be there before my brother Jeremy dies.

Upon arrival, I immediately crawl into bed with him and start singing a song that I sang to him often when he is a baby, *The Circle Game.*

And the seasons they go round and round
And the painted ponies go up and down
We're captive on the carousel of time
We can't return we can only look
Behind from where we came
And go round and round and round
In the circle game

So the years spin by and now the boy is twenty
Though his dreams have lost some grandeur coming true
There'll be new dreams maybe better dreams and plenty
Before the last revolving year is through

Jeremy, this boy, is now twenty-five and the revolving year is through, this is the last season.

Though he is now blind, he hears me sniffling to hold back tears while I am singing.

In his classic Jacky Mason old Jewish man manner, he squawks, 'What! You have a cold? Are you trying to kill me over here?'

) ((●)) (

While we are sitting down as a family for the traditional *Shabbat* dinner, he is upstairs in his bedroom slipping away.

We are somber, crestfallen. A sibling suggests that we each wear a hat from his eclectic hat collection on a hat rack in his bedroom. We do, and can't help laughing all through dinner. Perfect madness.

The days pass. He can no longer communicate by moving his finger to indicate yes or no. I let him know that it's ok, he can go now.

A few hours later comes an ominous and disturbing sound as his lungs fill with fluid. The Death Rattle.

I run around the house trying to reach my father, my other siblings, find phone numbers, leave messages.

The African hospice nurse, in the traditions of her faith, the South American housekeeper, on her knees, and my father with the traditional Jewish liturgy, all begin to pray.

The immediate family has all arrived in time. We surround his bed.

He passes. I close his eyes.

) ((●)) (

There is a custom, *shomer*, watching over a body before burial. Because I think this is what my brother would want, I ask the funeral home if I would be allowed to spend the night. Because they know and work with my father, they make an exception.

Most of my family thinks this is 'creepy', but this night, my father decides to join me, sharing a definitive moment of hallowed peace and space in between the weeks of tumult before Jeremy's death, and the following throngs of visitors over the seven days of grieving called *shiva*, yet to come.

These moments with my father are liminal. We won't share another night like this until many years later when he is in the hospital with a heart failure during Passover. The rest of the family and friends are participating in the holiday *seder*. My sister finds me a cheap flight from LA, she books the day before, and my brother drives me directly to the hospital. My father and I will enjoy a few rare uninterrupted hours together.

I share my stories with him. I tell him of the old lady and her scattered belongings. His eyes widen as he recalls his grandmother who lived with him growing up. He explains that she too was troubled by a similar experience as her neighbor's things were tossed to the street upon her death.

"I haven't heard anyone ever speak about this until now! That is so strange.' He reflects.

And at the end of the night, with great excitement, he says, 'I feel like I am meeting you for the first time!'

) ((●)) (

Jeremy's funeral procession is miles long. Passers-by think it is the funeral of an esteemed dignitary.

One thousand people come to the house that week to pay their respects. Stories are shared.

The dental receptionist recounts this: 'Your parents were away and left Jeremy the car. He had a dentist

appointment and it was snowing that day. He tells me that his parents left strict instructions- do not use the car, especially if it snows. So I said, 'So you walked here, right?'
The Yiddish old man voice retorts, 'NO!' His hand gestures, eyebrows furrowed, 'I took the car!'

A women comes to say she heard about Jeremy's passing. She wants to pay her respects because, one day while she was out working in the sun, planting shrubs for her mother's memorial, Jeremy came over to her, a complete stranger and asked what she was doing. When she told him, he said he wanted to help and stayed for hours planting. She came to tell my parents the story and of his kindness.

Jeremy, with no filters or restrictions, had no choice but to ignor all social decorum or norms.

He was known to walk into a neighbor's home and take a drink from the fridge, but managed to endear himself genuinely with all whom he encountered. No one could resist his purity and piety. He spoke openly and treated everyone based on their character, not their position in the world. He humbled the exalted, exalted the humbled. Many felt that they were in the presence of a saint, albeit, a whacky one.

) ((●)) (

After the funeral, a week of *Shiva* and then Passover, I arrive back in Los Angeles, unable to locate myself in time and space, along latitude or longitudinal lines, reminding myself frequently where I am. LA, Venice. Here. Now. Where?

Anxiety attacks begin. It takes me three hours to get out of my apartment- can't decide what to wear. Nothing is right. I change my clothes over and over again. I finally get out, then, at the curb, pause, sit. Can't move. Go back inside. Repeat the process.

This eventually gives way to manic-depressive states. Ecstatic when I paint, and then, when the brushes are put down for the day, I become stone, falling in a spiraling descent which leaves me paralyzed on the couch.

A friend suggests lithium. Oh, dear!
It seems I must do something. Take action.
Analysis of the situation is required.
Systematic inquiry.

A physical problem? My environment?
All indications are negative, no threatening danger. I'm in a comfortable Venice apartment on Rose Avenue, rather delightful in fact.

Mental? hmmm.
No issue here. I seem to be fine at carrying out the duties of my job, thinking rationally, paying bills.

Emotional/Spiritual?
Ding ding ding. Yes, Houston, we have a problem.

Now what? What does one do to combat such a matter?

A coffee shop barista recommends the book *Conversations with God* and *The Power of Now.*

After reading the first chapters of *Conversations with God,* I slam the book closed. 'That's nice, but I need my own conversation with God.' I head to the beach.

I am more than surprised when I 'hear', or rather perceive, a voice answering my questions!.

So, I ask, 'How is Jeremy?'

'Do you want to ask him yourself?' The voice replies.

'Uh...Okay.'

I apologize to Jeremy for the ways I feel I have failed him.

Ten years his senior, he was like my baby. I feed, dress, change him.

He has brain surgery in a NY hospital during the epic snowstorm that winter.

When he comes home from the hospital, at two years

old, his soft curly brown hair has been replaced with a large raw baldhead and a scar at the nape of his neck. He is bloated and crippled from steroids, nauseous and irritable from chemo. My parents cannot discipline him. So I do. I remove him from the kitchen table, he in a highchair, when he has tantrums, dragging him to the bathroom when he curses.

As he recovers from surgery, I walk behind him up the stairs, lifting his lame foot to strengthen it and get him accustomed to using it again.

But, I move out at eighteen and things change. I send him sketchbooks for self-expression and he fills each one with his language of cartoony depictions.

Between moves from Berkeley to LA, I return to New Jersey to be with him for his last summer. He hates me being there, makes comments and leaves hostile notes in the kitchen, 'Don't burn down the place.' 'You smell.'

He had always competed with my dad, desiring my mother's complete devotion. It was a tense and antagonistic relationship. His full-blown Oedipal complex proved Freud's theory of the Oedipal complex correct. The trauma of his illness seems to freeze him there. He suggests that he wants my father dead and casually mentions this at family dinners.

Jeremy transfers his anger to me when I come home before I start grad school to be with him. This has the unexpected and ironic effect of freeing up the space for Jeremy to have a loving connection with my father. I receive all of his anger and frustration at his disabilities- his scrambled egg mind, his stunted body.

I arrive home one evening to see Jeremy resting his head in my dad's lap as they watch a ball game together.

I would endure this painful summer a hundred times again, for them to have bonded as they did.

Jeremy asks my dad, who has always worn a beard, to shave it off, so that he can see my fathers full true face. My dad complies.

During Jeremy's last days, while in a drug induced state, he mumbles to me, what sounds like, 'I love you.' My sister and mother are there too. We glance at each other. I accept! I'll take it!

This reminds me of when Finn tells me the same thing while inebriated. I'll take it.

In my perception, attempting communication with the voice on the beach, Jeremy does not appear as my younger brother, broken and suffering, but rather, he is handsome, dressed in blue and gold robes. An unexpected idealized version and vision.

'Oh, that's all behind us', he explains, 'human things. There is work to be done. We have been waiting for you to reach out.'

'Should I tell the family that I saw you?'

'I think they need to remember me as I was.' He advises.

When he was alive he'd babble, 'I'm older than all of yous!' Now I understand. He is.

The day after Jeremy dies, the TV on the tall dresser in his bedroom turns on by itself. I am standing by the doorway, thinking, 'Oh that's Jeremy.' It doesn't even seem unusual in the moment. It would continue to go on and off over the next few years, especially when someone would stay in his room, or when my mother missed him more keenly.

Grieving with particular sorrow one night, my mother is sitting in her car pulled up in the driveway. She sees lights flickering from his bedroom window above. The TV is on again. She finds this comforting. Others in my family are sure there is some very rational reason for this occurrence.

I move to live by the ocean and wear Lolita de Lempicka, inspired by the folklore of the sea, Lolita Lempicka... Lolita Lempicka, I repeat the words. Chosen for its enchanting scent, balancing woods with florals, and for the sound of this name.

L de Lolita Lempicka

Top: bitter orange, cinnamon

Heart: immortal, vanilla

Base: precious woods, solar notes, musks

) ((●)) (

It is my first New Year's Eve in LA, and I am despairing for all things lost. I go to the ocean and spontaneously call out into its darkness.

'What do you want from me? WHAT - DO - YOU - WANT - FROM - ME?'

What I don't expect is a response. A boisterous laughter comes out of the blackness.

What the F***?

Two merrymakers, though it is too dark to see anything, call back to me. Slowly they emerge from the inky waters, assuring me that everything will be fine, laughing and frolicking towards the shore like Shakespeare's fools, dissipating the drama with absurdity, and the absurdity with truth.

The divine responded. The divine was drunk.

That New Years I meet an acupuncturist, later to become a boyfriend, who will fill me liberally with fistfuls of herbs and stick me with needles to keep me going for the next few months. The awkwardness of being face down as he pricks me full of pins is not lost on me, it adds to my already vulnerable state, yet is needed all the same.

Zygote, a eukaryotic cell formed by a fertilization event.

This is a process of cell union and division where two make third, which is a one, that will strive to be or become part of two.

Maybe, since I am already like two, Bonnard and Marthe, Narcissus and Golmond, Herman and Renée, then this cancels out becoming a two. Because being one of two, is like bookends, which is really two halves. Think about it.

I loathe the idea of being one that becomes two that is reduced to half. I'd sooner remain one, or find a one that becomes two which is really one. Together and alone.

Chicken or the egg? Which is the cause and which the effect? Ouroboros, the snake of Greek mythology, forever eats his tail.

Would I later take up a monastic existence because of barren romances, or is a life of failed relationships the only way for me to break free of some shroud of illusion, and to become a spiritual practitioner, my true calling?

All experiences lead the two parts to seize seeking for the purpose of adding and multiplying and adding, but rather to find the root number, to become one. And the one becomes ONE.
But then again...I'm not very good at math.

) ((●)) (

Los Angeles is my *Matrix* red pill, life accelerated. Fractals.

I should explain, that Berkeley was nearly my perfect life. I love everything about my time there, except that I know it will never be more, and somehow I know I am here for more, although am not sure what 'more' means.

Los Angeles, is indeed more.

I am Dorothy in gingham, ducking and dodging dodgy flying monkeys, confronting evil witches, exposing false prophets, seeking assistance from good guides of the North, with various characters all searching to fill their deficit with what they hope will make them whole.

Silly Billy, you had it all the time. There is no place like home.

Sometimes I get drowsy in the poppy fields.

'Don't fall asleep now!' I plead to my lilting self, which just craves corporal comfort. To be lulled to s l e e p.
'WAKE UP!'

) ((●)) (

While chatting at the buffet table with a women I have just met at some old rock star party in Topanga Canyon, I explain that my life has turned upside down and inside out ever since I got to L.A. What used to be easy for me is now hard, and what was hard is easy.

'Have you talked to a psychic about that?' She inquires.

'And I became a psychic!' I blurt out.

We burst into laughter.

I have multiple careers in Los Angeles, as a Rabbi, performing weddings and *Bar Mitzvahs*, and even playing the role of a rabbi in a film with Mickey Rooney. I am a psychic, painter, journalist, screenwriter, filmmaker, teacher, nanny. But the film will never get released on account of some debacle with the producer who ran off with the money. Hollywood.

But, all will synthesize into one expression of true authenticity - emptiness and nothingness.

During some weeks between different homes, an old musician friend from Harvard Square, now living in an apartment off Speedway in Venice Beach, invites me to crash on his couch, warning me about the ghost in the basement.

Years later, when the veils between worlds become hypothetical and after I acquire some skills and experience in the spiritual arena, I remember the poor soul, the ghost, stuck in the basement of the building up the street. I call on my downstairs neighbor, Margo, a Swedish born seeing soul, to join me in an attempt to release him.

Margo gathers some trinkets in a pouch and we head over to Westminster Avenue late that night. We descend to the basement where the spirit explains his situation to her- there is a killer on the loose and he doesn't want to leave because he feels an obligation to warn others and guard the building.

Margo, married to an actor famed for a charachter on the Holodeck, among other things, explains to him that it is now safe and he can go. He does. Job done.

The friend who lives there reports when I check in, that the ghost has never been heard from since.
Mission accomplished.

Later, I hear more details about this story, which I discover, is an infamous Hollywood legend.

From a web search, I learn that in the early in the 1900's, Charlie Chaplin owned several of the large buildings along L.A.'s Venice Beach Boardwalk. At one time, used as bath houses and lodging for vacationers, today are apartment buildings for the local hipsters that inhabit Venice Beach. Many of the surrounding buildings near the famed 26 Westminster Avenue address are in Chaplin's films where he filmed a great deal during the early 1900's.

During the shoot of *By the Sea*, in 1915, Chaplin's body double and long-time good friend, inexplicably disappeared from the film set.

Production was put on hold for three days as authorities began a man hunt. When nothing was found, it was assumed that Chaplin's friend must have quit and left. The studio that was financially backing the film was losing money so Chaplin replaced his body double and moved ahead on the film.

On the seventh day since the disappearance however, Chaplin returned to his dressing room, after a day on set, located in the basement of building, now a laundry room. I read that it is documented that 'Chaplin, while accompanied by an entourage, entered the room to discover his body double and friend lying dead on the floor, arms and feet bound, soaking wet, and tangled in seaweed, appearing to have been deceased for several days.'

It continues to be a mystery how this man ended up on the floor of Chaplin's dressing room after being missing for almost an entire week.

My loosely tangential connection to Chaplin will extend as there are still more ghosts to release.

Here, within the walls of the two story bohemian cafe on the edge of the western world, books and scripts are written, music composed, films envisioned and footage edited. I never meant to be here, but fate, with a different plan, has gently coaxed me here- tricked me really.

Some of us stridently impose ourselves, diving into our future. I, on the other hand, follow breadcrumb clues. And like a penguin, will wait for the path to be revealed.

While sitting at the cafe counter writing, an acquaintance, a ruddy faced bald headed man with a South Boston accent, who will later ask me to play Rabbi Schechter in his indie film, offers me a copy of Final Draft, the industry standard screenwriting software.

'I don't want this.' I decline.
'Just take it.' He coaxes.
'I don't want it.' I repeat.
'Just take it.' He persists.

After three times, I begrudgingly accept the gift thinking, 'Well, I guess I'm supposed to write a screenplay. Shit!' That seems like a lot of work.

It is.

Three months later, I begin *Weight of Light*.

CHAPTER SIX

eden burning

each Cobbler

Ingredients:

- 1/2 cup unsalted butter
- 1 cup all-purpose flour
- 2 cups sugar, divided
- 1 tablespoon baking powder
- Pinch of salt
- 1 cup milk
- 4 cups fresh peach slices
- 1 tablespoon lemon juice
- Ground cinnamon or nutmeg (optional)

Preparation:

1. Melt butter in a 13 x 9-inch baking dish.
2. Combine flour, 1 cup sugar, baking powder, and salt; add milk, stirring just until dry ingredients are moistened. Pour batter over butter (do not stir).

3. Bring remaining 1 cup sugar, peach slices, and lemon juice to a boil over high heat, stirring constantly; pour over batter (do not stir). Sprinkle with cinnamon, if desired.
4. Bake at 375° for 40 to 45 minutes or until golden brown. Serve cobbler warm or cool.

Friend, ex-tanglement LJ, while pointing out my fundamental flaws, explains that I should learn to cook. And while I will eventually enjoy this activity, mixing potions like an alchemist in my postage stamp size kitchen, astounding myself with my culinary achievements between two and five a.m., I will completely forget how to cook, however, when this phase is over.

But, at this juncture, I swallow formative feminist notions and earnestly attempt baking my present lover a homemade peach cobbler to the specifications of the musician's southern roots. I consult a cook at a local Southern restaurant to guide me personally for authentication, taking careful notes for an entire dinner. I carry this out at a neighbor's kitchen, as I don't have a working oven, who oversees the protocol and execution.

He is furious.
No, Really.

'Why did you make this for me?' He scowls, counter to his otherwise amiable seductive self. 'What if I don't like it? What if I do like it? You are trying to make me fall in love with you! Are you trying to make me fall in love with you?'

Way out of my element, I wonder, how humans do this-this date, relate, mate thing? Really, how?

I remember an earlier observation, which is now a fully developed conclusion: Women are fucked. A lose-lose paradigm.

I am fucked. And I am fucked. Though I earnestly try to extricate myself from the diminishing equation. Diminishing returns. Diminishing self.

A male friend says to me, after miscommunication mayhem, that I am competitive with men. This comment is very odd to me and doesn't feel true, why would he think this of me?

It takes some time for me to understand why he would think this.

I believed that I have to be as good as a man to be worthy or deserving of his favor - a skewed interpretation of feminism.

I am embarrassed by my femaleness. Ashamed of my more muliebrity, feminine characteristics.

I remember being on a school bus as a child. I gaze

out of the window as we pass a woman collecting her mail from her road side mail box. 'I don't want to be a woman.' I simply conclude.

I am very dispirited at the onset of menses and adolescent angst, listening to the same album a thousand times, face down in the black leather couch.

Driving with Robert, a judge and lawyer who chose law in order to properly defend himself and his blackness, makes a wrong turn.

'I'm sorry.' I announce.
'What, what did you say?'
'I am sorry.' I repeat in a hushed tone.
'Why should you be sorry?' He asks concerned, 'You didn't do anything wrong. *I* made the wrong turn.'
I pause. 'My ex always blamed me for talking to him and distracting him when he drove, it was always my fault.'
'It's not your fault sweetie. Never apologize for that, you haven't done anything wrong.'

You see, according to psychiatrist and author Scott Peck, 'Neurotics assume too much responsibility for things that go awry in their life, while character disordered people deny responsibility, blaming others for their problems.'

W and I could agree on this one point, everything was my fault, because I blame myself and he blames me! 'Neurotics make themselves miserable,' Peck observed, 'Those with character disorders make everyone else miserable.'

Robert is considerably older than me. He is respectful and gentlemanly. He has already retired and unlike men my age, is interested in supporting my aspirations, as he no longer worries about his own, with nothing left to prove. But he is distant in his own way. Vietnam. Panthers. Saw and did terrible things. He makes me aware of the subtle and not so subtle forms of oppression, reminding me that women only got the right to vote in 1919.

How far do these layers go?

) ((●)) (

After a friend brings me to a past life regression lecture in San Francisco, I attempt to look beyond my own past, sitting on the back porch with a view of the enormous lemon tree with its own impressive history.

In a scene, I am one of many daughters of a wealthy sheik who is sending me off to marry. My face is

covered, only eyes exposed. I am silenced. I cannot speak to advocate or object, I can only watch my fate unfold. Or fold. Fold in.
We have been silenced for centuries.

During one of our late night walks, Finn, interested in unshackling society, asks, 'How are girls silenced?'

'Well if you're a smart girl, you will be made to feel bad about it. And if you grow up to be a woman in a leadership position, with men working below you, you will be condemned for doing your job. Conversely, if you don't take the power and authority of your job, then you are criticized for lacking assertion and courage- 'Grow a pair a balls, would you?'

You learn to shut up and act stupid, and are faulted for that too.

So we are conditioned early on that we are only valued, and yet painfully judged, for our looks- and that is how a multi-billion dollar industry takes our money for lotions and potions, to fix what is not broken, to cure what is not sick, and we never feel good enough.And now we are broken and sick, which is wonderful because we will spend billions on anti anxiety, anti-depressants and therapy, so we will buy more shoes and clothes and keep trying to achieve an air brushed body. Go girl. You deserve it.

He tries to understand if being marginalized makes women care more about global and societal change.

I ponder for a moment. 'Maybe, if woman weren't so preoccupied, doing most of the childcare and household work while holding down a job, or being consumed by their appearance, frequenting the gym and salons for nail, hair, and bikini styling, in fear that not investing in appearances, to find and keep love, is risking all hopes of happiness.' I explain.

The revenue of the U.S. cosmetic industry is estimated to amount to about sixty two billion dollars per year. Vanity and fear are used to suppress our nurturing and gentle nature, turning them against ourselves and other women.
What would it be like if women were not engrossed with getting and keeping love and looks? What might we accomplish? I think of Aung San Suu Kyi, strong and feminine, winner of the 1991 Nobel Prize for Peace, undeterred, her hair customarily pinned up in the back with fresh flowers.

I recall the image of myself as the sheik's daughter, fully covered, except for eyes to witness.
Yet, no one to tell.

This vision, true or imagined, allows me to fully comprehend with compassion, the remarkable, sacred and fragile opportunity I have in this life - to paint, make films, write and publish, with the body and voice of a woman.

So, I must be gentle, patient with myself for this jagged, narrow and tenuous path just behind me. And the one still ahead.

Sitting with the boys at the cafe, they forget I am from the tribe of femme, commenting on every female that goes by. Judging, joking, mocking, socking- skirt too short, laugh and point, skirt too long, laugh and point.

Impossible to win approval and gain trust from the other side.

I internalize misogyny.

I meet a martial artist, driven, angular, wounded man.

I mention to him that he judges women.

'I don't judge you.' He says.

'Yes you do, you just judge me favorably.'
(For now).

Silence.

) ((●)) (

I do quite well with five year olds.

One only has to win a child's trust once, and though it might take a while, it's for life.

This is not so for the matured of our species - one needs to win trust constantly. It is tiring and disheartening. So, I prefer the company of those under three feet tall.

I make an exemption for one with a six foot wingspan and hands that feel safe when he holds me in the early morning hours, except for the occasion when he spreads his enormous wings knocking me out on impact, like an air bag during collision.

I become friends with a fourteen-month-old girl with aquamarine eyes, who squeals upon seeing me, pudgy arms extended.

Not so him. Calculated meeting of the eyes, perfunc-

tory, how are you's, not waiting for a reply, head down, back to work or out the door for a smoke.
Lamoure.

Love American style.

Upside down world, as Rabbi Yosef explains in the Talmud- *Olam Hafuch.*

I get dizzy.

) ((●)) (

After tasting the confection, the musician gives my peach cobbler an 'A', rating it 98%. But, he intentionally denies his love all the same, admitting that during that summer he had in fact begun to fall in love with me, but aborted it, refusing to love me in 'that way'.

) ((●)) (

Screenplay:

Weight of Light

INT. BORDERS BOOKSTORE. NIGHT

Myles and Ani on a date at the Santa Monica Promenade. They are browsing in the bookstore while waiting for their movie.

MYLES

Have you read this one? I think you would like it.

Myles points to a cover.

Ani is searching the Astrology section. She pulls a book off the shelf on relationships.

ANI

Here, I am looking up our composite astrology chart.... says We are 'great lovers.'

MYLES

That is true.

ANI

Don't you see 'lovers' as two people in a relationship?

MYLES

We are in a relationship, aren't we. We don't need to be married, do we?

ANI

There is a big difference between married and banging boots a few times a month.

He takes her hands.

MYLES

You know how I feel about you baby... you know that I love you...

ANI

So if you love me why don't we move forward?

MYLES

I love lots of women... besides I am seeing someone now and it might get

serious, but I always
want you in my life.

Ani looks pale. She is speechless. Myles looks at his watch.

MYLES
Hey babe, we need
to leave now if we
are gonna catch that
movie.

These scenes repeat verbatim with different men. This is not only seriously weird, but agonizing.

This loop makes me want off and out.

) ((●)) (

I don't know why when I throw colors at your feet you glare at me white faced.

) ((●)) (

The paralyzing thought of walking in front of a bus whispers in my mind for months. This terrifies me, because I begin to believe that it is me that wants to do this. I can no longer discern or recognize an external agency or demon who wants me out of the game.

I hate living on planet earth.

I concede however, in better moments, that there are some lovely bits - iridescent sea anemone that cling onto the jutting rocks that I eagerly seek out on beach walks towards the Venice Pier. Willow blooms and willow trees in the Boston Garden, night jasmine that keeps the same hours as I do, surprising me when I walk by on my way home from the cafe. The glowing sunset painted on airborne seagulls during the magic hour, ruby throated humming birds that come suck at the red bottlebrush flowers outside my door. Cello music.... and pots of tea that I take exceedingly strong, with milk and honey.

In fact, Finn and I often reflect and marvel over the Camellia Sinesis shrub, and remarkable alchemical potency of this truly simple pleasure, as the skyline changes hues.

Lapsang Souchong.

The story goes that the tea was created during China's Qin dynasty when the passage of armies delayed the annual drying of the tea leaves in the Wuyi Mountain. Eager to satisfy demand, the tea producers sped up the drying process by drying the tealeaves over fires made from local pinewood giving it its signature smoky flavor.

Smoky tea.
Smoky eyes.

) ((●)) (

Once when I am caught between worlds, when this one seems far too static and slow compared to the dimension I have entered, like a wrong floor that I have stepped out of on an elevator, where all things that ever were exist simultaneously in a paisley dynamic swirl. I look out of a moving car and remember, 'But, this place has a night sky.'

For years that follow, I am reminded about this strange event every time I exchange departing words with a friend named Sky, uttering 'Night, Sky.'

After returning here fully, a process that takes some days, I eventually, and with much resistance, appreciate that things happen here consecutively, seemingly in a progression of isolated moments, making it possible to truly have an experience, saving it as such.

Garlic sautéing in butter, oil paint mixed with turpentine, wrapping myself in a warm sheet just out of the dryer, the sound of snow falling like tiny bells in the distance at two a.m.

At the bus stop waiting for the Big Blue Bus, a women wearing a yellow mini skirt and black tights crosses the street just as a mini cooper the same colors passes, or a twenty-five year old man throws a ball and gestures for it to come back, not realizing anyone is watching him, and a couple pushing a stroller with identical twins down the sidewalk, followed by their twin dogs on leashes, both in red harnesses, and the parents, also, like twins, carrying identical umbrellas, both in matching blue sneakers, and blue sun hats.

Some weeks after the strong urge to walk in front of a bus, I pass by a bus pulled over at an angle in the middle of the street.

A man is pinned by the bus and then dragged for a block before the unassuming driver is alerted by a driver behind him who sees the young pedestrian run over.

A streak of blood lines the street.

I don't understand at first why I had stumbled into this tragic episode, sitting transfixed as police arrive at the scene, quartering off the area. Fire trucks follow, a helicopter above. The police on duty are visibly distressed by the event, the driver, sick over the situation is taken away in an ambulance.

It seems like a higher self or some disciplinary deity is reprimanding me - 'See! This is what it looks like to be hit by a bus. Still think it's romantic? A good idea? It's selfish. Look, look closely. Pay attention, selfish woman!'

I do, shaken and nauseated.

From that point forward, I never fantasize about walking in front of a bus again, but take with me the chilling memory of that May afternoon, as a defense against demons who might try to convince me otherwise.

) ((●)) (

Midsummer, ahead of schedule, after I finish 'Quantum Messiah', a screenplay about Jesus, my hands keep writing.

This is the result, children's stories for my young students.

The Ssslithery Sssneaky Ssserpent Ssssnake

My name is Sai Tan the Ssslithery Ssserpent- Sssnake.My job is to see if people know the difference between GOOD and EVIL. And if they do know the difference, I test them to see which they choose.

Ssssometimes it's really easy and kind of fun too.

But Sssometimes I need to be Sssuper Sssneaky and I have to try Sssuper hard to get a person to do the wrong thing.

I'm actually rather famous. Perhaps you have heard of me?

Ya know, the story of Adam and Eve?

That was Sssuch along time ago.

My first big job.

God had just created the world and everything was Sssso beautiful then.

The Garden of Eden was Ssspectacular in every way.

Waterfalls, wild flowers, fruit trees, Sssparkling Sssstreams and rivers.

It smelled like jasmine and honeysuckle and sounded like birds and babbling brooks.

Adam and Eve were very happy there.

They climbed the trees, Sssplashed in the lakes, and watched fireflies at night.

But, there were two trees that were off limits.

The Tree of Life and the Tree of Knowledge. That was God's only rule in his garden.

That's where I came in. I convinced Adam and Eve to eat fruit from the Tree of Knowledge!

First I got Eve.

I Ssslithered over and just whispered in her thoughts ideas like, 'Who cares about rules?, We don't need to follow rules.

Its SSSO much more fun to break rules.'

Soon, she believed me! She started to think these were her thoughts and ideas!

That's when I know I'll win. Then Eve got Adam to break the rules too.

Humans can be Ssso easily tricked, Ssso easily be made to do the wrong thing, to make wrong choices, and to forget good from bad.

Of course, God was really disappointed and Sssad that his people could not be trusted to care for his beautiful garden.

I thought it was funny - They had to leave their paradise, and nowhere was ever as wonderful. Life was never that easy, fun and peaceful. Ha!

Ever since then, I have tricked lots of people and made them do terrible things. That's why people fight, and why we have poverty, pollution. And then I just sit back and watch.

I'm really that good!

But, between you and me, I have a Sssecret weakness- If you have a bad thought, and say, 'I know it's you Satan, you can't fool me- that's NOT MY thought!

Then I will disappear in an instant, because I can't stay were there is TRUTH and WISDOM or near a person who has a GOOD and PURE HEART. It makes me freak out, faint and fade.

It's HORRIBLE.

Sssso now you know, about the famously talented Ssslithering Ssserpent

Sssnake who Sssearches to find Sssomeone to trick.

But don't tell anyone else, because if enough people know, humans might live in Eden again.

) ((●)) (

'I'm going to tell!' shouts out one girl, six years old. 'Me too.' Chimes in another. My dearest kindergarten class, after hearing this story, shares and confesses how the snake tries to trick them, and that now they will know what to do.

) ((●)) (

Since the early part of the 21st century, the Demon of Pornography, which proliferates and transmits by subcontracting other demons, including, lust, greed, misogyny, anger, insecurity and humiliation, has grown exponentially.

Pornography alone, will be responsible for the destruction of romantic love in the human world as we know it.

This demon removes intimacy from the most intimate expression, demotes humans into objects, promotes disconnected sex as the ideal, turns bonding into bondage; deems public what should be private, commodifying that which is free, putting monetery value on what is priceless.

Where I had once tried to make peace with this demon, I now commit to annihilating it with superhuman and supernatural strength.

I learn to use my palm erect like a sword during meditation.

Bean soup.

The musician is touring on the other coast. I am on the phone with him while stirring a big pot of bean soup.

'I would do anything for a bowl of that soup.' He says, like Esau before him.
'Anything?' I ask.
'Anything. M, if you get me a bowl of that bean soup by midnight, you can have anything you want.' He says.
'What's the address?'

I'm weak for dares.

He laughs and indulges my daring spirit the way he

likes to indulge in most things.

The next few hours are a series of phone calls to the hotel concierge, room service and the hotel kitchen staff, which I learn, is out of vegetarian stock.

At three a.m., I get a text and a photo of a bowl of bean soup in his room when he gets back from his gig.
'Do you have anything to do with this?' He texts.

The next day he is sitting with his band members for breakfast before the sound check. Their admiration and fascination of this woman grows, he tells me. As does his anxiety.

When he returns from his trip we meet at the trendy Urth Cafe where he, nervous for me to collect on my winning request, asks what it is that I want. I suspect he thinks I want a marriage proposal, or worse, which in his estimation is hard to fathom.

What I want is in here.' I tell him. I give him a wrapped box. He opens the box, and confused, replies,
'But M, there is nothing in the box.'

'Here' I say, handing him an envelope.

Opening the card, he becomes even more baffled. The inside of the card is blank, I had written nothing.

He urges me to explain, 'I don't understand, there is

nothing here.'
'That's what I want from you- NOTHING. I don't want anything that you won't freely give me.'

When we say goodbye that night, standing at my front door, the two of us seemed indeed close to tears, because we both know that I have set him free. He is free to go live without commitment, and I am committed to live freedom. He, eventually, will marry someone else, but still texts me on my birthdays.

I will learn other skills.

Like Bill Murray's character in Groundhog Day, who learns to play piano and creates elaborate ice sculptures in his ever repeating day. Where killing himself doesn't save him from waking up to the same day again. I learn qi-gong, start a non profit organization TRUTH on TOUR, raise my moral character or heart nature, write screenplays, make a documentary, and learn to make pie everything. Pot, shepherd and apple.

I learn to layer flavors like color, spices like cardamom, curry, za'atar, paprika, basil…juniper berries and dark cacao…

I make soups, lentil and minestrone that I share with my Venice neighbors in need for one reason or another.

And its the same day.

And I agree with Janis Joplin, who I imitate with surprising parity, through the halls of my patriarchal parochial high school shouting, 'Its all the same fucking day man.'

) ((●)) (

On a particularly treacherous pass, as my peers are progressing with tangible and status raising careers and families, and I, having dropped out of Rabbinical school, dashing the only plan that would enable me to raise a family on my own, I need to know the truth once and for all, no matter how grim. I am prepared to hear it -

'Am I really a loser? I consult my heart, 'tell me, I can handle it?'

The answer changes everything and my life makes sense in a way it had never before.

'You came here to know your self worth, with nothing else to affirm you.'

In that instant, radical clarity.

I had needed to learn the nature of my intelligence, as I had been a dyslexic who had grown up believing that I was quite stupid, after constantly failing tests and classes in school. But, I was indeed, in many ways successful though always broke, talented though not famous, nurturing though without child, The list is long.

'I have nothing. So, I am actually succeeding.'

'Exactly.' The voice-thought confirms.

Illimitable revelation, paradox, relief.

I make strides on all fronts to know my true self-worth. But, it seems conclusive- if no man chooses me, I must not be lovable, this de-saturates the color from my life, a flat monochromatic world I'd rather not live in.

Finn tells me about catching dorado fish, how their scales are a rainbow of changing color, golden, yellows, blues and greens, and that when it dies, it all turns to gray. He tells me how sad it made him.

That's like me in reverse, I say.

This would still take more time and more battling with demons than I could have ever imagined. This is the last gate for the romantic, the last relic of the human self, the last skin. But, the cerulean blue book could guide the voyage home.

) ((●)) (

I learn to forbear. This is the only thing that keeps me from committing unthinkable sins during the demon invasions, the teachings from the little blue book, cerulean blue with gold lettering, the book that espousing Truth Compassion and Forbearance. I come to see that only forbearance can thaw the icy wastelands I seem cast away to live in. And compassion will slowly melt the frozen landscape into clear crystalline water, then primordial water, where I will return.

The blue book could quell Lilith, a demon I first encounter in my twenties when my first love fathers a child with another women.

Lilith, according to legend, is the first wife of Adam, but as the story is told, refuses to lie beneath him and is therefore deemed unfit as Mother of All. So, off she goes. Enters, Eve.

I can feel Lilith's frustration, heartbreak, and rage at being so misunderstood over the millennia.

When this boyfriend, from the Wampanoag and Cherokee tribes, gets another woman pregnant, I don't know where to put the brewing madness from anger and hurt. I have dreams that while caring for the baby, instead of the bottle, I put the baby in the microwave.

I create a series of paintings, constructing huge urns on canvas from drips and strokes and dabs of color.

I know Lilith well, have pity on her, aware that poor Lilith is a repository of every injustice paid upon a woman - every lie, deceit, abuse, rape, betrayal.

The Cherokee and his one-night stand, have a son named Gabriel, and I can only bless the boy who is given the name of an angel.

Around the same time I get a job caring for the son of a ceramicist and an admired Boston painter, who has a studio in my building.

When I show up one morning to babysit, there are people there that I don't recognize. They let me in, but there is whispering and confusion.

No one has remembered to call me.

The boy, Nico, just three months old, has died a few days ago.

I am told that the mother wants to see me. I am one of the few people who knew her son, so I am allowed to enter the closed door to her bedroom. From the bed she recounts to me the time I sat with him on my lap soothing him, as his first teeth came in.

The curtains are drawn that gray autumn day, where she lays in bed, in the dark with crushing pain, breasts engorged with milk. The milk keeps coming. The empty cradle still at her side.

I have never seen such a cruel sight.

The painter's friend, a poet from Yale, reads an eloquent poem he composed at the funeral about a life that only knew love. I sob and then paint a huge urn for the baby in ultramarine blue and pale creamy yellows, naples and hansa.
It is W's favorite painting.

In the Charlestown studio, that I share with a photographer who has me pose for a series of portraits, I paint the diptych 'Eve and Lilith' with fleshy pinks and foliage green.
Sometimes I still feel Lilith thrash beneath my skin. When I close my eyes, I can hear her shrieking in unhuman tones, the shrill hollow writhing of unimaginable fury.

My hands become tremulous in Lilith's presence. I knock over a tea cup and a box of tacks, and as I replay the events over, I know there is no apparent reason for the accidents, and do not see how my hand would have made such erratic gestures. It is Lilith quaking about, smashing against the edges, like a trapped bird surrounded by windows trying to free itself amidst the illusion of open sky. But Lilith is humiliated by the ordeal. She too can fly, though no longer fooled by the illusion, is unable to escape all the same.

) ((●)) (

'To be a woman is to be humiliated,' comments the young Turkish photographer with teal eyes, who possibly shares a past life with me in the mermaid colony and who certainly shares the haunting of baby turtles.

) ((●)) (

Marley says, 'Give me a kiss goodbye.'
I roll my eyes, suddenly I am all the boys I hate.
She is my friend Sila's sister. We work in a sandwich shop together.

She is like a young Ann Sexton, the poet, with an electric guitar.
She is in love with me.

I try to wrap my mind around such a configuration. Everything is coming into question- identity, sexuality. Would I wear cologne to appeal to a woman? Stop shaving my legs? Why do I do anything? Conditioning, forcing me to examine the calling of my true nature. I compromise, shave my legs but leave my underarm hair.

Marley moves to northern California while I am in Boston. We hadn't talked in a year when we finally get in touch. We have a sweet conversation at which time I have a flash- I hear the thought, 'She was so happy the last time we spoke', things you say when someone dies.

Marley died three days later, stabbed to death. It was presumed an attempted rape.

I gave her family the paintings I made of her when she posed for me sitting in the ocher chair in her charcoal blue gray trousers, falling asleep. I enjoyed capturing her square jaw and dark thick short hair, angled over her big brown eyes, as she appears in a few of my paintings.

I have a post card from the Trident bookstore of a young Dorothy Parker, the author, that reminds me of Marley. I don't know anything about Parker. Years later I discover they both shared sarcastic wit, both are half Jewish on their father's side, and literary.

Sila tells me that the day before her death, that Marley was visiting her grandmother and woke up describing a very strange and vivid dream - she was in the most beautiful room filled with golden books, and everyone was there at her grandmother's and it was very hot.

The funeral was during a heat wave during early fall in Northern California. Everyone at the funeral was foretold in the dream. I imagine she is in her gilded library reading the books that do not yet exist.

) ((●)) (

I grow up with the children of my father's colleauge and dear friend. In our early twenties, we suddenly become fascinated with each other. Jon, in his yellow print ties and suit, and me, in a vintage blue taffeta dress with a netting petticoat detail, pearls beaded near neckline scoop. Opposites attracting.

He is in New York. We speak on the phone. I plan a trip to visit him at his grad school in early October. I have to cancel the trip because this coincides with Sila coming to town, for a memorial for Marley. I can't meet him.

This very weekend, Jon meets someone else, they will marry and have a baby boy around the same time my Cherokee ex-boyfriend has his child, a baby boy. This is around the same time that Nico, the child I adored in Boston, dies.

These events, three boys that are not mine, being born or passing on, leaves me with the message that it is not my time to have my own child or to take care of other people's children either.

Focus on art.

It seems it would never be the time to have my own children and always the time to focus on art. Yet thousands of children will pass through the radius of my influence and will flourish.

CHAPTER SEVEN

book wrestling

I'm a stranger in a foreign land and although I seem to speak the same language, I don't understand.

This foreign place is school.

I am a character in my own imagined sequel to Camus' book that I am assigned to read in high school, but never do.

Why would someone who claims to be an existentialist bother writing a book in the first place?

School is the first box.

People banter around the phrase, 'Think outside the box.' I didn't know there was a box. I don't know of this common system.

Some of us are born in the box, some are herded in soon after, while others need maps and instruction for finding it and operating within its proximity.

Some of us need this instruction drawn in colorful pictures depicting icons and landmarks associated with related emotional resonance. Some need mathematical equations, precise data with circumference for comfort. Some prefer nautical, elemental references, including the movement of stars, time of year for bird migration and weather patterns.

Still others need it sung in a lullaby.

How does one enter The Box, and what might the consequences or rewards be for doing so? Can you get back out once you get in, are there emergency exits, public transportation, equal access for all?

Kindergarten is lovely, but all becomes alien thereafter.

I'm not indifferent, just different.

In third grade, I wonder how everyone else knows what to do, when I am so lost. We build a huge Noah's ark. I make the lions. This, I get.

My father asks about my homework assignments. I don't know. Why don't I know there are homework assignments? He is frustrated, loses his temper with me. I feel bad that my smart papa has a dud for a

daughter.
I burrow deep into myself.

In high school, I sit down to study for a final exam, pulling out the year's notes, all utterly incomprehensible gibberish, turns me cold and sick inside.

Like the moment we find out that Jack Nicholson, in *The Shining*, has spent all his time writing a book comprised of just one sentence, 'All work and no play makes Jack a dull boy', repeated a bazillion times.

That sick feeling.

Frightening- because this looks like the writing of a mad person.
I burrow deeper.
Never tell anyone.

But as an art major, I get into university. My personal essay and portfolio are strong. In painting class, I come to sense my intelligence.

I feel like NASA, discovering intelligent life, my own.

It has its own way of organizing, perceiving, analyzing, it doesn't live in my mind, no, somewhere deeper.

I will cherish and slowly learn to trust it, defend it, cultivate it, as it cultivates me- moving from the non-verbal languages to the written, expanding into my mind and heart, eyes and hands and into empty space.

At eight years old, I am fascinated with the back cover of a children's scrapbook that my grandparents buy me. It is decorated with astrological symbols and signs. The written word, now, begins to interest me.

I read my first books in my twenties.

Astrology books allow me to match my own perceptions and knowings with the written words before me, creating a symbiotic relationship between my thoughts and words in reverse, a process which will eventually begin at the written word and lead to comprehension.

For the fist time, the written word, this collection of letters and symbols, has a relationship with something I know. A pathway is forged in my mind for associating words with cognitive ideas and thoughts. Though decoding is still arduous, with effort I crack the codes.

My mind doesn't build files. So, like a computer, if there is no file or system to save it to, bye-bye.

I don't make this connection until after an entire summer of trying to organize my apartment, I find at the end it is no more organized than the day I started.

I walk around with a photo album or box of chargers and extension cords, trying to figure out where it goes, can't decide, and pick up another object. Weeks of this makes Jack a dull boy.

) ((●)) (

To support myself through college I get a job teaching at a religious after-school program at a synagogue outside of Boston. But I am ambivalent about being a teacher, since I had loathed school. I feel like a traitor.

There are children and there are grownups. Us and them.

I cannot conceive how it can be that grownups don't remember how it was to be a child. Do they really forget? How does this happen?

When I am still a child, I wish as hard as I can to imprint this on my soul and mind, instructing my future self never to forget being a child.

This may be in part the reason it is easy for me to connect with children.

I never forgot. And I don't forget.
And some things about teaching become evident:

1. I have the opportunity to make school for others what it never was for me.
2. Whatever I hope to achieve as an artist happens more readily, efficaciously in a classroom.

I can create a small community of joy and expansion, honoring the individual, while working and sharing together as a collective.

I spot all the kids who are drifting away. I see their maneuvers to keep me off their trail, so that I won't suspect they do not understand the lesson.

I know where they are, I know how they feel. I know how to bring them back.
We expect children to meet us where we are. That is impossible.

Like someone adrift on a raft in the ocean, it's a search and rescue mission.

We must get into the cold water with a life jacket in hand, because they are scared. They would rather fail from not trying, than fail after trying, because that is too humiliating. They will do what they can to avoid any more bruising. Protecting their fragile ego.

Because I am them, I know how to find them and get them safely back to shore. I won't let you drown I try to say to them in the silent language of my gaze.
Ich und Du, I and thou.

In this space created between us, the atoms that will form pathways, bridges, avenues trails and rails. Seeds yielding life.

While working with children I will often sense the profound field that is created, and the words I and Thou, coined by Vienna born philosopher, Martin Buber.

My first awareness of Buber is in a Jewish Encyclopedia, where in volume 'B', there is in an old photo of Buber from the early 60s. My young father's face beams out from among all the parade celebrants at the side of the eighty-year-old philosopher!

Without having read his work, I sense that this is in part Buber's thesis, his foundation. Success lies in the space between. The mutuality. Where, sharing that same space, rapport is experienced. Then, can come communication, where all is possible, a third entity of commonality. The new color made between two primary colors. The fertile green ground of potentiality created between yellow and blue.

The students, like works of art, require similar skills from me. It will be a dance between my will and their potential- a process of discovery.

Eric:

I was asked to tutor Eric, athletic, magnetic smile and sweet nature.

He slips through years of Hebrew classes without learning how to read. Now, I am hired to catch him up, prepare him to come in front of the community for his *Bar Mitzvah*, leading and chanting prayers and scripture in Hebrew.

I work with Eric and he makes great strides. When I move to LA, another teacher takes over for me. She calls me and wants to know the secret of my success.

'How did you do it Masha? Did you find out his diagnosis?'

'No,' I explain, I have a distrust and disinterest in diagnoses. They are too often wrong.

'Then how? You did really well with him. what did you do?'

'I played football with him', I answer.

'What? Football? What are you talking about?'
He is athletic, and I show up on the football field, looking inept where he is a star. I'm on his turf, willing to be incompetent, willing to look foolish. So, he is prepared to take a risk with me, in my classroom.

We are equals, willing to go beyond protected boundaries, defended borders, trusting that the other will gently guide us towards success with encouragement and aplomb.

I hadn't really had a plan, just instincts. I hadn't been trained, I was unorthodox, just showing up empty and trying to intuit with the children, something no one had done for me. My dyslexia creates empathy and understanding, but I have no direct or received method for guiding them through.

Lila:

A girl riddled with adolescent angst, hoody over her head, hair in her face, growling at everyone who attempts conversation with her. Time to intervene.

'It doesn't seem like you are having a good time here.' I say.

Grunt.
'But, I am working really hard so that you will have a good time and find this interesting.'

Rumble, mumble grumble.
'Hmmm. So, do your parents make you come?'

Head down, guttural, 'Yeah.'

Ich und du- I immediately get it.

'So, let me see, you have decided to hate class as a way to get back at your parents?'

Silence, but a smile can't help from peeking through the hood.

'So, no matter how much fun school is, you refuse to like it?' I jest.

Giggle.

'OK, lets make a deal, you can have as much fun as you want, and enjoy learning all you can, and I promise I won't tell your parents. If they ask me, how Lila is doing, I'll say, 'Oh, she's so MISERABLE.'

Big laughter.

Lila becomes one of my most diligent students, staying in during recess to do more work, usually art projects. I run into her years later, she is an artist.

Like the creation of art, each child requires my full attention of fierce perseverance and yet measured approach.

Maryanne:

I'm given a little room at the end of a long corridor, with a large old wooden desk and view of the front lawn, to work with Maryanne, who has caused her seventh grade teacher so much aggravation that I am hired to take her out of the classroom and create an independent study program for her.

Quirky, awkward and innocently wholesome, like a cross between an adolescent American Girl doll and Woody Allen, she bubbles over with observations and ideas that she can't contain. Constantly erupting and interrupting her teacher. As a result, she is now with me.

How to affirm her unique character and preserve her enthusiasm, while teaching her to be aware of others, and acquire a sense of appropriate boundaries.
I embark on 'A Place to Put' therapy. Like I had done for myself in the studio, like I had tried to do with my brother Jeremy. We create little notebooks for her clever ideas, so they will not be lost, and instead of being shamed for her ideas, lead her to listen and respect other peoples ideas too, while respecting and honoring herself.

I experience the metaphoric as literal. The language of *holding space,* and *giving space* feels actual. I learn that my energy can amplify and swell like a basin, created for others to fill with their own energy, as my energy spreads out to the edges of a room. Energy is felt and perceived, not rationally known. I do not withdraw or abandon Maryanne, but rather contain her safely while giving her all the space and structure she needs to bring herself out, find the scope, shape and color of her own energy.

I learn to do this for myself. Providing myself safe spaces to create from. Demanding excellence and creating a scaffold for success.

Carla:

The third grade has 'free art' this day, with colored pencils, markers, and crayons, drawing anything they want during this allotted time.

I walk up and down between the desks, looking at the varied work.

Carla, a quiet Indian girl, has drawn a thin purple line surrounding a figure.

'An aura?' I ask.

Her big brown eyes meet mine in delighted surprise. 'Do you see them too?'

From that point on, whenever I teach her class, she and I play a game, I ask her what color my aura appears. One morning she tilts her head, 'That's funny,' she observes, 'one side is light green and the other side is blue.'

A professor at Rabbinical school says my presence gives other people permission to be themselves.

Laura:

Laura's parents' divorce leaves the five year old needy and prone to tearful outbursts.

'I miss my Daddy.' She sobs, just after he drops her off.

I intuit a strategy to help Laura cope with 'feeling out of control' being away from her parents.

I teach her to use the clock hanging on the wall behind her.

'Your father will be here when the big hand is on the six.' I explain. She watches and tracks the movement. Now, she can pace herself. She has something she can count on, quantifiable, measurable. Her tears stop.

Life becomes a little less unpredictable. She isn't a victim of circumstance in an ocean of unknowns, now she can be brave. She can be a hero in her life, conquering the fear, the loneliness, the tears.

I apply all of these lessons to myself.

With Rabbinical aspirations and schooling, I sometimes tutor and officiate the Jewish coming of age ceremony for those thirteen years of age, a Bar and Bat Mitzvahs.

Many of the tweens I work with are outside of the synagogue school system for one reason or another - a parent not Jewish, kids with learning issues, or the child that surprises parents by wanting the ceremony when the family is not particularly religious.

Because many of the students have no Jewish background, my lessons encompass everything from reading and writing Hebrew, learning about holidays, customs and liturgy, while preparing for the ceremony that they will lead in English and Hebrew.

We often meet at coffee shops accompanied with warm sweet drinks and pastries.

Each child is a riddle with a pad lock keeping them from full success. I unscramble codes and unlock each child, one conversation, lesson, or exchange, at a time.

Ich und Du

Mitch and Devon are twin brothers. One is very sensitive, polite, deeply moral. The other is sweet natured and only interested in baseball. Neither one wants to be studying for a Bar Mitzvah. Both are only doing it for their parents.

Mitch is certain this is not for him, but reconciled. He

finds religion superfluous since all humans, in his estimation, know innately how to behave and do the right thing.

Dyslexia teaches me that, because I don't have answers like a glossary of terms I can retrieve on demand, I am empty, open with receptors up. I understand I need to approach each child on his and her own terms, comfortable with not knowing. And, through listening, with the desire and faith to prevail, there is only the *Ich und Du.* There, I will find the answers, in the space between us. All is revealed.

Writing the *Bar Mitzvah* speech offers great opportunity to crystalize and articulate beliefs and ideas. It is a way to forge the nascent adult identity, affirming the individual within the context of family and community.

The individual within society, a balance we have not been able to quite achieve. A society which prizes the self at the expense of the greater collective breeds sickness, but also, failing to value the individual weakens the strength of the collective. Middle path says Buddhism, middle path.

Mitch expands on the idea of empathy 'You know the feelings of a stranger, for you were strangers in the land of Egypt.'

Devon recites, 'I discovered that Judaism and baseball

are similar in simany ways. Baseball and Judaism both have rules which allow everyone to play together, a way to measure yourself, and a standard to strive for.
Both try to push you to be your best, the rabbi is like a coach, they can giude you, try to help you improve, but it is really up to you.'

After the service, I overhear Mitch say to his younger cousin, 'Are you going to have a Bat Mitzvah? You should, it's a lot of work but it's so worth it.' He sees that I overhear him. I lower my eyes, smiling in my heart.

Everyone has given up on Alex having a *Bar Mitzvah.* He is now fourteen.

I am told his 'condition' prior to our first lesson. He is diagnosed with mild Asperger's. He needs structure, I am instructed. Well, if that's what he needs, that's what we will do. So, although I am more fluid in my approach, I will adapt to him, I will meet him.

But, structure is not what he needs. During my introduction, I outline in detail a very regimented schedule, and at the end remark, 'But, I like to be open to inspiration.'

He smiles saying, 'Yeah, that works for me.'

I ask him to repeat this, making sure he heard and understood.

We never have a rigid schedule from that day onward. He thrives. What I learn about him is the opposite of what the specialists advise. His emotions are very strong, if not addressed at the onset he is moody and unfocused. He must identify his feelings, needs, options, solutions, choices. We have incredible success, and fun. He is philosophical, creative, sensitive and sincere. He craves to express himself, to be heard. As do we all.

Maddie is bright and sassy. Her father is a professor of neurology and she, with the mind of a scientist and the attitude of a Westside girl, thinks that God and Hebrew school is a waste of her time. For weeks I try to find a way to reach her, bring her into the conversation. I explain that her agnostic voice is relevant and welcome in our class, that she too is an equally valuable part of the class. This doesn't seem to mean anything.

I am losing her. It is like struggling with a painting. I will not give up.

We are making a short film based on a line from Deuteronomy, 'Love God with all your heart, all of your soul, all of your everything.' I open a conversation with her saying, 'This project might be challenging for you to work on since you don't believe in God.'
'Yup.' Only half snarky.

'Let's see if we can figure this out, a way for this to work for you.'

We discuss theology, science, creation, belief.

She is unsure.

'So, it's a mystery to you?' I reframe.

'Yeah.'

'What if we replace the word God for 'Mystery', I suggest. Instead we will say, 'I love The Mystery with all my heart all my soul and all my everything. Would that feel right for you? Would that work?'
Bingo! Game changer! Maddie, is able to find integrity and meaning in her studies from this point forward.

The *Bat Mitzvah* makes sense as she can place herself comfortably in the tradition. When it comes time for her Bat Mitzvah, she uses the term, 'The Mystery' in her speech to the community, she learns her material quickly and easily.

Establishing trust is paramount.

Carl Jung believes and trusts implicitly that his patients must and will arrive at the right decisions on their own.

Since this marks one's journey towards adulthood, I point out that this is a good example of exercising adult wisdom.

There is a time I had abandoned *Ich und Du*, and the consequences are not good. When I seek advice from 'the experts', my life lessons overwhelmingly expose their deficits, imploring me to trust my own wisdom.

A teenage boy directs a comment to me during class, 'I thought of you the other day- in my bed.'

I consult the school therapist. 'You need to talk to him, tell him this makes you uncomfortable.' She insists.

I ask to speak to him after class and it's awkward. I'm uncomfortable. These are not my words, my real sentiments. He looks shamed, mortified. He thought he was being cute.

My discussion with him hadn't come from an authentic

place in me, or acknowledged our genuine connection.

Sometimes, I handle sexual inappropriateness with a bit more levity and mastery. Two boys in the back of the seventh grade class attempt to shock me.

'Masha, is penis a bad word?'

'No, penis is my favorite word,' I respond.
Screams from the back row. They babble and yell, arms flailing in adolescent gainliness.

'Are you serious?

'No sillies, let's get on with work.'

I never have a behavior problem again with this class. Putty.

And then there are the teachers that are pivotal in *my* life.

Geraldine Jackson, five feet of feisty, with pixy short hair and reading glasses that slide down a slightly pug nose. Lean and sparky. Often scary.
She is the math teacher. I am a computative disaster. She puts me in the lower group and ignores me. The

next year, she teaches English.

There is no awareness of different learning styles at this time. I assume stupidity is the culprit.
'She's sweet, creative.' Is the best a teacher can say of me.
I am even a creative speller!

Every week Mrs. Jackson gives us a creative writing assignment. One week, though mine is short, my story on re-gifting makes her laugh. She reads it to the class. I am now on her radar.

From this point forward, I rise and rise to the bar set before me, becoming one of the two highest graded students in the class for creative composition. Myself and my friend, Missy.

I am not much for competition, more the Aphrodite than the Athena or Artemis. I am thrilled for us both. She is driven, petit though complains she is fat, frets about failing tests when she will score a ninety-eight.

Chances are I will score a thirty out of a hundred and I am woefully chubby. Eleven years of age.

Bits from my first poem for Mrs. Jackson:

> There was silence,
> a lone snowflake
> from above,

a paucity of trees
stood tall and bare

birds in a paragon
across an empty gray sky
There was silence.

The thesaurus is now my trusty companion, my favorite game - the wonderment of words! I seek them out, hunting words like a scavenger, a canine on the trail, a pirate for loot 'n booty. Then, savoring the delight of the hunt, I tack them to sentences like animal heads to plaque and wall.

My treasury of gemmed jewels to which I will devote myself first comes in the form of the sixth grade Friday creative compositions where, I pull all-nighters, writing and rewriting.

Here, it starts. Deep into the hushed amorphous night, I am most awake, discovering shapes in the shapeless, word-less, time space, planting and harvesting in the rich fertile darkness. I am free.

Construction of the bridge begins.

I am born into the tribe of Israelites, the Children of

Israel, people of the book.

Israel, *Yisrael* means 'wrestles with God.'

What does it mean to be dyslexic as one from the people of the book?

I'm one who wrestles with books.

Every child, a combination lock of fear and societal restrictions, wiring, firing, concealing talents and abilities within. I am a safe cracker.

Ruby of Bella Coola is a screenplay I write for children:

A locked girl gets un-so, and finds her power and true self with the help of some mentors.

Ruby of Bella Coola 1 pager.

```
Genre: Fantasy, martial arts, coming
of age, drama, family

Logline: A young adopted Chinese girl,
a product of the persecution of Falun
Gong, learns the magic and majesty of
```

her lost heritage when the Chinese cast and crew of a Hollywood film come to her small rural hometown of Bella Coola, BC. But, the martial artist star might learn even more.
Tagline: Magic is not what tricks you learn, but the truth you awaken to.

Themes: Ancestral roots, innocence of children, connecting to the magical ways in every culture, adoption.

Synopsis: Ruby is a nine-year-old girl from a small town in the Western coast of Canada with no summer plans. She keeps to herself, feeling out of place in a town comprised of Caucasians and native Canadian tribes.

For four weeks, a Chinese martial arts film star is filming on location in her small town, with the Chinese cast and crew of his new film, 'Demon Mountain,' in Bella Coola, a remote area of BC.

As the only person of Chinese heritage in this small town, Ruby, who has always felt 'an outsider', forms a precious bond with the Chinese cast, who teach her the ancient ways. The seamstress on set teaches her about the dynastic ages, the cook teaches her Chinese cooking and about Lau Tzi, the Chinese Confucian philosopher. She joins them for qi gong tai chi in the mornings and learns about the tea ceremony from the art director.

Ruby's innate innocence and awakening supernatural abilities makes a believer of the old, jaded actor who had sold out for money and fame. The two are enriched by their encounter as the girl, no longer lonely, discovers a rich magical world within herself and the actor returns to his true nature as he remembers his youth before the Chinese Communist Party stole his belief in magic.

Another teacher, who is able to 'see me,' my value, is Howard Zinn.

I take a class with the famous historian and activist during undergrad at BU. We have two assignments for the semester - keep one journal for volunteer work and write one about the classes and the reading assignments.

I hand the journals in to the Professor's assistant, whom I know from the vegetarian dining hall on campus. The teaching assistant wants to meet me.

'Mash, you can't hand this in, you are missing all the reading assignments. You need to redo this.'
I haven't done any of the reading, I don't own the books, because I don't understand what I read. But I don't mention this. 'Just hand it in as is.' I say.

My journal includes illustrations. I draw a pencil sharpener and write the name Howard Zinn connected by an equal sign.

In one journal entry, I explain that I have decided to pull my head out of my intimate Bonnard prints and expose myself to a wider breadth of education, more global in scope. In the future, I will move between the poles - micro and macro.

Mr. Zinn comments that he and his wife have a Bonnard print in their bedroom over their bed. On the front page he writes, 'A'. Not for content but for eloquent honesty.'

CHAPTER EIGHT

the evil eye

The market price for Falun Gong harvested organs.

Cornea: $30,000
Kidney: $62,000
Liver: $98,000–130,000
Liver, Kidney: $160,000–180,000
Kidney, Pancreas: $150,000

It is at the cafe that LJ tells me that Falun Gong practitioners are being tortured in labor camps in China. He stirs his coffee, extra sugar, extra cream.

I am stunned, only knowing a little about the Falun Gong practice from him.

He moves out to the West Coast on my invitation

and arrives after three days on a bus to stay with me indefinitely. Personal conflicts strain our entangled friend-ship wreck, but, in this moment, as he conveys the details of a brutal persecution, all personal matters dissolve and I am overcome with compassion and sadness.

'What would make a government act so viciously towards its own citizens?' This is my first thought. It's only a moment before I connect this to the Holocaust that I grow up acculturated in - commemorations, museums, Anne Frank, proclamations of 'never again.'

LJ, a practitioner of Falun Gong, or Great Way, and part African American, cannot help drawing immediate connections to lineages with a legacy of persecution.

My heart breaks then.

I am raised educated on how governments fashion campaigns for political agendas, manufacturing reasons to hate, demonize, propagandize, fabricating lies.

Although I am not particularly interested in this practice, rooted in eastern schools of Taoism and Buddhism, the sinking feeling doesn't leave me. I start reading their guiding scripture, the little blue book, Zhaun Falun, to understand.

) ((●)) (

I have adopted a 'One Hundred Monkeys' philosophy that refining, healing and changing myself is the most effective way to make lasting positive change globally.

At first, along with the 'veggie' cronies, those of us from the vegeterian dining hall, I protest at various college events. But a visit from my roommate's older sister enlightens me that these issues are more nuanced and complex than I realize. This valuable lesson gives me pause. If I am going to be out protesting, I really ought to understand the issues. Responsibility. Integrity. Basics.

Around the same time, during a humanities class, the professor mentions that the mystics believed that the best way to make changes in our world, was to influence the realms above, or more accurately, realms beyond. This makes perfect sense to me.

So, I refrain from large-scale activism, making personal revolution my action towards human evolution, only striving to align and connect with the benevolent invisible forces at work.

Until one day, I act.

) ((●)) (

'Of course, the Chinese government would not allow this!' I surmise after reading through the blue book.

This is a most powerful teaching, the kind that grounds a person in courage. This is in direct conflict with the Chinese Communist Party, CCP, who maintains power by instilling fear.

Like an abusive spouse, they will separate people from their support, severe roots, sun and rain.

In the coming weeks I learn the history of the CCP. They are in clear opposition to the Falun Dafa guiding principles: truthfulness, compassion, tolerance. I will begin handing out flyers to inform people at the Santa Monica Pier with some of the other adherents.

I distribute copies of 'Nine Commentaries' too- a highly articulated document published by the Epoch Times on the nature and origins of the Chinese Communist Party. The result has been a total collapse of social, moral, and ecological systems as well as a profound crisis for the Chinese people—and indeed for humanity. All of these calamities have been brought about through the deliberate planning, organization, and control of the CCP.

Rumors begin to surface that the CCP is using detained Falun Gong prisoners as a live organ donor bank. David Matas, a Canadian human rights lawyer and David Kilgour, retired Parliament member, are asked to investigate these allegations.

While handing out flyers about the persecution to

tourists and natives on the busy pier, I listen to their questions, and hear their resistance and disbelief.
I listen.

An acquaintance, who knows my fine arts background, with connections to the paper, invites me to contribute to the Epoch Times Arts and Entertainment section.

This paper, is started by Chinese people living in the US, as an alternative to Chinese media, otherwise censored by the CCP, with the intention of exposing China's lies and deceits to its citizens living outside the mainland. Now, it is in over thirty countries and eighteen languages.

'Sure,' I think, 'I could write for a paper.'

Then I think some more, lying in bed making mental bullet points like bullet holes, numerating reasons why I can't.

I can't spell, I can't type, I don't drive. I have no experience, I'm not smart enough. I'm too shy,
I can't... I don't… I'm not …I can't….I wont…..

This internal barricade barrage makes me acutely aware of a tenacious multi tentacled belief that needs to go.

To remedy the 'I can't disorder', I will systematically

say 'yes' to everything presented to me. This proves to be a transformative experiment, leading me to make RED REIGN, a documentary about the forced organ harvesting, and will cure me definitively of this 'I can't' malady.

Adolescents and the twenty-something's struggle to find and claim identity, to belong, to categorize themselves into distinctions, hoping to fill in the blanks, proudly asserting with conviction and resolve- I am-, I like- I don't- , I won't-, I never-.

Once my persona strengthens in my thirties, I am able to make proclamations like, 'I am a vegetarian, I never wake up early. I don't cook', I figure, it's time to null and void them, to challenge and expand these notions which are now only limitations.

We are so much more than any of these labels.

This is how I come to put away the paintbrushes. I recognize that I was extremely identified with the idea of myself as a 'painter.'

I stopped painting and sat at cafes for weeks wondering who I am and what I do.

Lost, but space was created.

That was when I was asked to write for the paper.

So, engaging in rigorous examination and evaluation of everything I think- everything I think I know, everything I think I am, when making conclusive statements, I try to be less absolute, using words like 'prefer' and 'usually'. Even moderation is done to the extreme.

Exceptions are made, however, for the declarations such as, 'I operate best in or near water' and when watching my favorite film, I have a desire to swaddle myself in that film.

And, I take, on average, two baths a day, not as a cleanliness obsession, but rather like eating sorbet in-between courses.

) ((●)) (

With 'yes' as an answer to all propositions and requests, I continue to connect dots.

Dot 1:
Although as a journalist, I mainly cover arts and culture events, I occasionally report on other events as needed.

This day in April 2008, I was needed.

By line: Masha Savitz
Epoch Times Los Angeles Staff. Apr. 6

SANTA MONICA, CA. Banners filled the grassy lawns with messages of, 'No Human Rights, No Olympics', and 'One World Equals Human Rights', on a sunny Sunday afternoon near the entrance to the Santa Monica pier.

The Human Rights Torch Relay (HRTR), set against the pacific coast, officially began with a powerful drum procession escorting a white robed 'Goddess of Justice' and the glowing torch she carried to the stage.

Los Angeles resident, Dana Churchill, presided over the event, comparing the upcoming Beijing Olympics to 1937 games in Nazi Germany, adding 'when kindhearted people stand up for persecution, they are considered political.' Churchill introduced the numerous and impressive panel of impassioned speakers and performers, addressing concern or outrage over China's human rights abuses specifically in light of this summer's Olympics in Beijing.

'We have built an economy in China totally ignoring the fact that the Chinese government is still run by tyrants and gangsters. We have now given them great power and great leverage to use, not only to keep control in China, but now in a way that threatens all of us and threatens the whole world.'

At this Rally I meet David Matas, Nazi hunter, human rights lawyer.

) ((●)) (

Figuring that he doesn't know anyone in town, I invite David to join me at my cafe. He agrees.

From time to time, we email. Sharing an interest in films, I ask what he has seen lately, and where is he on this day. His itinerary is mind-boggling. His commitment to human rights is breathtaking. His film reviews, better than mine.

Dot 2:
When in February of that year he is nominated along with David Kilgour for a Noble Peace Prize for his work investigating the organ harvesting of Falun Gong, I consider, perhaps this could be my new project. And, if so, this is the time.

Dot 3:
So, I am at the cafe, musing on possible future projects when a successful Canadian producer, a friend of mine, comes through the door.
He is very enthusiastic about fellow Canadians David Matas and Kilgour and their recent nomination.
He wants us to work together, encouraging me to go for it, but he goes instead, back to Canada to reconnect with an old girlfriend.

I wait for him to get back in touch while searching for grants to proceed on the Red Reign documentary project. But, he never does. And I don't get grants. With no experience making a full feature documentary film, I am on my own with a learning curve resembling a ninety-degree angle.

Walking along the Jasmine-lined Venice street near my home, I find a charm on the pavement with the word 'trust' engraved into the tiny silver plaque. I wear it everyday forward, losing and finding, breaking and fixing this reminder frequently.

Trust is what guides this creative endeavor and the main factor for its success.

Screenplay:
Quantum Messiah

ARCHANGEL GABRIEL
In the time of the
human world when a
new era came to pass,
great Masters walked
the earth, leaving

teachings to point
towards truths from
beyond this realm,
pointing to the way
home, and setting
the stage for things
still yet to come.

For this is the great
last act, the final
play.I was there
then, and have
witnessed the
unfolding since.

) ((●)) (

I am in New York attending a seminar as a writer for the Epoch Times, when a coworker suggests that I join a workshop for the sister TV station NTD, New Tang Dynasty. I hesitate, as this is out of my arena.

'Just go, you never know.' She says.

My 'just say Yes' mandate has me jumping on a train downtown on a bitter NY winter night to engage with a different medium, media, meteorite showers.

I walk into the 'introduction to editing' class. I take one look at the rainbow colored grid of timelines and the multitude of buttons and switches of the editing interface and I walk back out.

I will never fully escape editing, nor will I want to.

I am first introduced to film editing when I meet Finn. He is working on his film and I am mightily intimidated by his editing software. Finn is a musician and composer among other extra/ordinary accomplishments such as boxer, horse trader, and sailor, before he sails to LA, where he reinvents himself as a screenwriter and documentarian.

'It's easy.' He always says, 'easy.' Eeezy.

Neither Finn, nor editing, are always easy. But things of great worth usually are not.

I commit to the Red Reign documentary.

Here we go.

An earnest and bright barista at the cafe wants to sharpen his editing skills and offers to help me create a trailer. We put together, albeit clumsily, a trailer which becomes the foundation of the official trailer. I embark on the full-length documentary.

Needing feedback, I send the trailer to Finn, who at that point hasn't been to the cafe in quite some time.

He stands at the curb in front of the cafe having a smoke. He says, 'Masha, I feel a little guilty, I kept telling you how easy this is... and well... it's not that easy... and now I feel like I have to help you.'

In the days of the Great Jerusalem Temple, a guilt offering was called the *Asham.*

This is even better.

After spending a good part of the first year applying for grants and working on the four-minute trailer, I feel like I will never finish the trailer, never mind the film. And with anemic finances, it seems terribly irresponsible to use my own money on such an expensive venture.

Eventually however, it will occur to me that it isn't a matter of using 'my money.' It is all just money sent my way, after all. All things given to me to use for Good. And this is surely a good.

So I jump in and venture forward with no resources to speak of. One hundred percent trust.

Until I don't.
Doubt dominates.

Nothing looks favorable, no funding, support or skills. During serious reflection, I wonder if I might have been mad when I decided to make a documentary.

Had I experienced an episode of momentary insanity? No, really.

I fully consider this point, evaluating my state of mind, retracing that moment of decision with great acuity.

I discover, conversely, that everything has led me to this project like a finely laid, manicured path of the dots that I connect: my painting background, an upbringing which emphasized justice and Holocaust education, LJ moving out west, writing for Epoch Times, interviewing doc filmmakers, an established doc filmmaker who took an interest in the project, watching Finn make his film, learning how to use a camera, meeting David Matas, friendship with Canadian producer Amos. Dot, dot, dot.

With this securely in my mind, I never doubt again and never look back, solidly pushing forward from that point forth.

Because, women who look back turn into a pillars of salt, the salt of the tears shed in regret and sorrow, rage and horror.

This is a painting that I make in a Boston studio- a very ambitious undertaking, a triptych of Lot's Wife. Three large panels of reds and pinks sewn together with gold wire as she turns back, witnessing her village, Sodom and Gomorra, ablaze.

I am hired to help another filmmaker make editing decisions on her documentary. She can't let any footage go. I learn to be a surgeon, cut what must be cut. No place for squeamishness. Invaluable, as I hone the skill of storytelling, concise and clear. We need to shave twelve hours of complex medical explanations into informative, coherent selections.

I get many part time jobs, working constantly for months. The exhaustion effects my performance directing a shoot. I am not a workaholic, I tell myself, it's just that my ambitions, ideas and faith are greater than my talent, resources and skills.

I am willing to accept the hardships. It's a Jewish thing I guess, a sort of conditioning. But I am trying not to be complacent and suffer unnecessarily - a Falun Gong thing, to let go of conditioning.

Because, although I don't object to suffering entirely, the work quality can't.

'If this is the path for me, I happily accept it." I state to whomever is listening, the divinity on duty, or assisting angels. But, if you have a more efficient way to make money, I will happy accept that too.'

The next week I am called into the office at the school where I have been teaching a class. It is explained to me that the school director has been let go, that it didn't look like he would finish out his contract, and might I be able to take over his position, part time, in the interim.

I respond that I am in the midst of making a film and have other commitments that I will not abandon, but I will serve in any way that is helpful.

My income increase as well as my responsibility. But as the pressure increases, I wake and fall asleep with tears in my eyes, trying to meet all of my obligations and

finish the film, which seems unfathomable.
But miracles increase too. A Venice friend, KC, offers to foot the bill for the Winnipeg film shoot.

The first big shoot is in Winnipeg, late December, one of the rare times that David Matas is home for a few days in a row. KC lives for a good adventure, and over the years he and I have shared many. He is eager to support this one, taking charge of the three-day shoot.

I purchase a full length navy wool cape from a thrift store to layer over sweaters and thermal everything.
We meet at a hotel in Winnipeg, and while warming up later with chai lattes, strategize the shoot before picking up cameraman extraordinaire, T, who flies in from New York City. The team is assembled and the temperatures are favorable, hovering just around freezing point and below. Ha! Any colder, and T is sure the equipment will freeze.

We shoot the footage that will form the backbone of this 'no-budget' film: Interviews of David in his modest office and home, and B roll footage to be inserted as cutaways, to illustrate the story.

It snows while we are there and I am very excited about the visual possibilities. With such a dreadfully difficult subject, I want beautiful images. A frozen Lake Winnipeg, snow and ice, just the right feeling.

T is frustrated with me. He wants more decisive

instructions.

I ask, 'Can you get this shot?'
He says, 'Do you *want* it?'
'Well, I wouldn't ask if I didn't want it.'

Ah, styles of communication.

I track my feelings here. He, an Israeli man, of similar look and sound to ex-husband W. This provokes the fear that if I tell him what to do, I will be punished.

Other female directors are also punished for doing their job.

It is the day before Christmas, the last day of the shoot.

In gratitude, I take KC shopping at the downtown mall to find perfect gifts for his family, a chore he spurns. The store is filled with refugees from around the world in their colorful patterned garb, brilliant against the Winnipeg gray.

I buy David a silvery blue paisley tie for Chanukah. 'You a painter.' He says when I present it to him, out at dinner before I leave.

He wears the tie in a newspaper photo I see later that year.

The B roll shots are challenging. I wince at the idea of 'literally' portraying this story, as the visual images are far too graphic and disturbing.

Harley, a millennial in the neighborhood, with an interest in biology and things edgy, shows me her book of Renaissance anatomy illustrations. I will use these for stills!

These beautifully rendered drawings will solve the aesthetic challenge, beauty whenever possible, to counterbalance the CCP's destruction upon lives, tradition and art. These classical images will be used in the film over the description of skin and organ removal.

I first become aware of Harley during an ordeal in the neighborhood. She is stoned out of her mind with cronies six floors up on the roof of an apartment building. One of the girls jumps, or falls. Only the heroin knows for sure.

Harley is strung out, and panicked as police seek to interrogate her and her romantic interest.

In a few years, she will get sober and become licensed as a paramedic, like those who came that day, when the street was roped off and no one knew if the girl they took away had lived or died.

She did live, and woke from a six week long coma on her birthday.

) ((●)) (

Making the film is a brutally lonely time, as I need to cut most people out of my life.

There have been other such times in my life, when I know, that to succeed in doing what I know I must, I have to tune everyone out. I too possess that 'male preservation', and access it on this project.

I become myopic in focus. My usually diffused awareness is sharpened into a compressed beam of light, due to both a lack of time to socialize, and because of the subtle, and not-so subtle hostility projected onto one who dares.

I need to protect myself and the project, precious, important and fragile, from the 'evil eye.' My childhood nanny in Turkey, Nazle, had given me a little blue amulet fashioned like an eyeball with an azure center for protection against such threats. In Jewish superstitious traditions, this evil eye is referred to as 'ayin ha'ra', and this eye seems to be squinting at me.

Nazle, I recall only from childhood photos, is the round old woman with a kerchief, who gave me the small charms as an infant that I grow to cherish as I get older.

Friends who haven't claimed success for themselves or achieved their own dreams are the worst enemies to those who risk and do. I feel the hostility, arrogance, and jealousy, critically accusing me in harsh tones, warning me that I will not succeed.

As I already have plenty of doubt, additional cynicism from outsiders insinuating 'Who do you think you are?' cannot be afforded.

I wage constant war against discouragement. There is always a million reasons to not try. If you want a reason or excuse to give up or never risk, there will always be a plethora.

And sometimes, there is only one reason to act - because its the right thing to do. This thought alone trumps all others, summoning legions of light beings, angels and gods to help.

But the dark forces want in on the game, too.

So it is 'on!' and I am in.

) ((●)) (

Quantum Messiah

EXT. LAKE. NIGHT

The boat is already a considerable distance from land, buffeted by the waves with winds howling. Rain starts to fall.

Some force beneath the water is baring Yehoshua up.

Yehoshua goes out to the disciples, walking on the water.

The disciples see a figure walking on the lake. They are terrified.

DISCIPLES-LUKE, MATTHEW, ETC.
Holy shit! Oh my God,
It's a ghost!

YEHOSHUA
Have courage! It's
me. Don't be afraid.

PETER
Master, if it's you,

tell me to come to
you on the water.

YEHOSHUA

Then come.

Peter straddles the side of the boat to get out.

He too begins to walk on the water towards his teacher.

A gust of wind blows, the wave surges.

PETER

Help! Lord, save me!

Reaching out his hand, Yehoshua catches Peter.

YEHOSHUA

You have such little
faith, why do you
doubt?

They get close to the boat, and the disciples throw out a rope to help Peter into the boat.

As they climb in, the wind dies down and the rain subsides.

DISCIPLE 1
Are you really the
Son of God!

DISCIPLE 1
It is the Son of God!

Close up of Yehoshua, who appears in a vacuum.

Rain falls on Yehoshua's face, like tears-

YEHOSHUA
(Voice over, only the
audience hears)
I won't always be
here with you. I
won't always be
here...

) ((●)) (

I quickly learn that if I am to make a film that would affect many, I will need to become bigger than myself. Knowing the fickle nature of the film industry, I will need to suffer disappointments and the many factors that are out of my control, needing to trust others, figuring out which ones, and how much.

Finn will be an interesting experiment, as an editor. Accomplished in his own right, a strong man with strong ideas - how would it be to work with him? Would this powerhouse power over, coerce, co-opt? He will surprise me over and over again.

Like a good mentor, he never does my homework for me, though no doubt it is painful at times, or at least humorous, to watch me flounder.

He advises, we discuss, not always agreeing, but we always put art and purpose ahead of egos. He always honors my position as director and over time, he will redeem my faith in collaboration, in communication, in men and humanity. Mostly.

This is the fist evidence that my hope for harmony, born in the vibrancy of the Come/Union paintings, might exist- principals of polarities, complimentary rather than insulting.

My first musical impulse for the project, still just in conception, is to combine the sometimes sadly emotive but always ebullient Western Klezmer clarinet, suggestive of the influence of the Holocaust, with the hauntingly eerie Eastern erhu.

My family is planning a trip to Israel for the following

fall, for the Bat Mitzvah of a grandchild. Would I go on the family trip?

Notoriously reluctant to make plans, infamous for waiting until it is too late and absolutely uncharacteristically, I blurt out, 'YES.'

'That's odd.' I think to myself, 'There must be a reason I need to go to Israel.'

I will soon understand.

During the shoot in San Diego, shortly thereafter, where David Matas and David Kilgour are both giving a talk and interviewing recently released prisoners of Falun Gong, I reluctantly operate the camera myself.

A cameraman, whom I had hoped to hire with future funding, encouraged me to 'go shoot it myself' on the automatic Cannon I had bought online.

At lunch, Kilgour, a veteran Canadian Parliamentary Member, magnanimous, tall and slim with thick white hair, circles the table handing everyone paper napkins.

During the interview in the sun drenched South Western style campus, I ask which country was the first if any, to change policies on organ trafficking.
'Israel.' He responds.

There seems to be a few threads connecting the film

with Israel.

Liat, also an Israeli, is my footage 'go to' girl. We sit for hours at the NTD station pulling archival footage from my wish list. She is also able to make the necessary introductions and arrangements with Falun Dafa practitioners in Israel, who set up interviews with people pivotal to making these changes at the policy level.

It crosses my mind that Liat must have worked at the Akashic records in another reality. The Akashic records, the compendium in which the lives of everyone, throughout history are recorded, must be imprinted on massive cosmic hard drives.

We prove to be good friends, promoting the film together, educating people about China's massacre of Falun Dafa, and other horrible human rights abuses.

) ((●)) (

I have worked with words and color, and now notes and melodies, too, are a part of my creative life, and an important aspect of the work. This deeply delights me as levels of expression, communication and creativity layer.

For Red Reign, I point the sails in the direction of

composer Max Richter's soundtrack to a haunting and hypnotic composition. Much like the film itself, I want the music edgy but beautiful.

Finn suggests asking a young composer who frequents the cafe, J Shabo, to try his hand at creating the original theme for the film.

For nearly three decades, as writer and painter, I execute my vision alone. It is carried out in the studio between me and my notebook, sketchbook, macbook, and it is always a solitary endeavor. I had become accustomed to the belief that beauty could be mine, but only when I made it myself.

This moment defies these long held notions, because, on this occasion, Shabo delivers to me the most beautiful music, beyond expectation. I sit and listen that day with headphones on. Beauty I didn't have to fashion myself, but that was mine all the same.

Finn and I sit at the cafe to hear Red Reign's theme music for the first time. It is one of the best moments of my life, like my birthday only better - much, much, better.

According to Chinese legend, dragons carried pearls between their teeth. They must first be killed in order to retrieve the prized pearls.

Shabo slayed the dragon, or more aptly, composed the

music, which would help me to slay the Red Dragon.
This day I get a precious pearl.

) ((●)) (

Liat puts me in touch with Iris, a composer, wife, and manager of a famous Klezmer musician. She will organize the Israel film shoot with Dr. L.

Iris picks me up at Ben Gurion airport after midnight and takes me to her home for the night. She serves me Rose Chai Tea in the morning.
I am jet lagged.

Rose Chai:
I do a Google search and discover that the Wissotzky family, who made the tea, were all lost during the Holocaust.

We head off to interview Professor L, Director of the Heart Transplantation Unit at Sheba Medical Center, and a member of Doctors Against Forced Organ Harvesting.

Dr. L is welcoming and generous with his time. We meet at his office which is filled with heart memorabilia and art. I guess you could say heart art. He is eager to be accommodating, offering us a large conference room to shoot the interview. He shows me footage of a human heart injected with dye, the blue looping pumping heart will be used in the film.

When I interviewed David Matas in Los Angeles, he explained how the CCP employs similarly evil tactics as the Nazis to control the population - fear, anger, hatred.

As the intention of this project is to expose evil, evil interferes.

It will try to create miscommunication and discord between me and my team and any support, including the Israeli crew, where the shoot is nearly sabotaged.

Iris becomes infuriated with me. She thinks I live in New York and has therefore miscalculated our online meeting by three hours. Iris is crazy upset and frustrated having waited three hours for my call! I am disrespectful, she concludes.

This happens a few times before the culprit of the conflict, the time zone, is discovered. But it nearly derails this important interview.

Similar scenarios of misunderstandings occur making me want to quit, but I cannot be deterred from a mission so much bigger than myself. The gods of truth, goodness, and compassion will need to help.

At each step, I look within, clear out any anger, hurt or fear that may weigh on my newly forming wings, and if I can be clear and unmoved, then the gods can indeed step in and help mend the messes.

I write a children's story about documentary filmmakers and other messengers with difficult messages.

Jonah's Time Out

Once there was a man named Jonah.

God had special job for Jonah.

God needed a messenger, that is, a prophet.

God asked Jonah to go to the town of Ninveh and tell everyone to behave better.

But Jonah went the other way.

To get far away from God and Ninveh, he got on a boat.

Then a BIG crazy wild storm came.

The waves were crashing against the boat.

Everyone got very scared.

'God is trying to get your attention.' Said the sailors.
'You can't run away from God, and you are causing us a lot of problems. So here you go,' and the captain handed him a life jacket and tossed him off the boat.

'Yikes,' thought Jonah, as he went into the cold stormy water.

Just then, a HUGE whale came and swallowed him up.

'Yikes.' thought Jonah.

It was pretty quiet and calm in the belly of the whale.

But, there wasn't much to do. He could hear the whale gurgle, he could hear her heart beat.

He was getting a little cold, a little bored, and it was really dark in there.

'What are you doing in my belly?'

Jonah was surprised.

Again, he heard the low rumbly voice, 'What are you doing in my belly?'

'That's weird.' Thought the prophet who refused to be a prophet.
'I think God gave me a time out.'

'Why do you need a time out?' Asked the whale.

'Well, I didn't do my job. I ran away.'

'Why would you do that?'

'I don't know.' Shrugged Jonah.

'I guess I was scared that no one would listen to me, that no one would like me, that I might not do a good job.'

Jonah felt really bad. He let God down. He let the people of Ninveh down, and he let himself down, too.

The whale could feel Jonah's heavy sad heart, beating next to hers.

'God asked you to do the job Jonah, because he knew you could do it.

God wanted to see if you believed he would help you succeed.' Explained the wise old whale who lived DEEP in the sea.

'God wants you to be your BEST.'

'Really?'
'Really.'

'I have an idea,' suggested the wise whale, 'I will take you to Ninveh and leave you near there. You can still go and do your prophet job. It's not too late!'

So the wise whale brought Jonah to Ninveh.

The whale opened her enormous mouth and Jonah, a little soggy, walked out on her big squishy red carpet like tongue.

Jonah gave the people God's message.

And they listened to him, and they became kind, fair, and righteous.

And God was Happy.

Jonah did his job. And God was proud of Jonah.

And Jonah felt proud too.

And he never ran away from a job again, and he was never afraid to do the right thing, even if it

seemed scary, because he knew God would help him.
And late at night before he went to sleep, Jonah thanked God for believing in him, for giving him such a special job, for being able to remind people to do the RIGHT thing and to be their BEST,
just like his friend the wise whale did for him, during his time out, when their hearts beat together to the sound of God's BEST.

The footage has a low humming sound on the audio, rendering it unusable.

Troubleshooting for a scrappy unfunded film, I call T, Israeli DP, who did the Winnipeg shoot.

'Any chance you will be visiting Israel soon?' I ask. As fate would have it, T is going back the next month and is able to reshoot the interview.

In my email exchange with Dr. L to get his agreement, he comments that he wished that in his field he also had the luxury of a redo.

T successfully gets the interview and sends the footage to me.

One of the last parts of the filmmaking process is to laboriously write a 'time coded script,' required by the distribution company for sales with foreign networks who will need to create subtitles in their respective languages.

```
00;11,24;22 - 00;11,52;20

Narrator VO (voice over) Masha Savitz-
(that's me talking)

[B Roll: footage of Chinese people
going up an escalator]

'When we look at the facts surrounding
this issue, the conclusion becomes
hard to deny. One important fact
to consider is timing. The average
wait time for viable organs is quite
long because organs, suitable for
transplantation, must come from
healthy people. Consequently, the
average wait time, for a heart, is
eight months, for a liver twenty-six
months, and a kidney, a thirty-seven
month wait.'
```

No matter how many times I hear or see these words, I am still unable to fathom the barbaric nature of the CCP.

The time code is the number of frames that have gone

by in the film. Like numbers tattooed on an arm, or a political prisoner who has given up their name to protect their family, these numbers are now a record, a testament of these people's lives, and their suffering now exists in a documentary.
00;13,04;12

[B Roll: archival still of Chinese woman, jail tower, executed woman]

'Organ procurement, in China, from executed prisoners, had been taking place under official, legal knowledge of all authorities in China, and, actually, organs from these executed prisoners

00;13,18;00 -00;13,26;03

had been used for any patients, flocking from all over the world, who could afford to get a transplant from these prisoners.'

Iris takes me on a small tour around her home outside Tel Aviv. There are many music awards, which she explains belong to her husband, who, as it turns out, is a world class clarinet player, the King of Klezmer. Iris herself is an award-winning composer.

I was hard to contain myself, having wanted clarinet Klezmer music for the beginning of the film. But, I don't mention that. I discover later, that Steven Spielberg has had the same 'great idea' to feature GF's music in his Oscar winning film Schindler's List. This positions me two degrees from Spielberg.

Amazingly, Iris donates music to the film.

Still needing pieces of atmospheric music for background, I put out a call to the musicians of Truth on Tour. These are musicians from around the world, in all genres, who I had organized to create a CD and perform concerts to promote awareness about the situation of the Falun Gong practitioners in China.
Christpoher from Sweden, who is featured on the Truth on Tour CD, with the hip hop artists Arise Ascend, responds. I request something scary and something inspiring, and wake up the next morning to music on a file via email like it's Christmas, each perfectly perfect.

I write a children's story,
Here is a taste.

When G plays, his bouncy music floats out of his clarinet.

Sometimes the music is really happy and it makes everyone want to dance.

Sometimes the music sounds and feels a little sad.

But it always feels ALIVE.

The Psalm (a psalm is a poem-prayer) teaches that Music is a great way to express your love of God and God's world.

Psalm 150, says we should praise God with musical instruments.

'Praise Him with the sound of the trumpet;

Praise Him with the lute and harp!

Praise Him with the timbrel and dance;

Praise Him with stringed instruments and flutes!

Praise Him with loud cymbals;

Praise Him with clashing cymbals!

Let everything that has breath praise the LORD.

Praise the LORD!'
GF says that he uses his talents from God for a job.

Whether you play well or not, or who you are, is not that important sometimes. Everyone simply does what he was arranged to do. 'I was a great clarinetist, because God gave me a job.'

GF's music in the film is everything I had hoped for and more, creating a buoyancy and soulfulness.

Six Degrees:

The Truth Tour and Epoch Times leads me to connect with the famous violinist, Shenkar, who also uses his musical talents to promote human rights. I am 2 degrees from Peter Gabriel and his befitting song *Red Rain.*

> *"Well I've seen them buried in a sheltered place in this town they tell you that this rain can sting, and look*

down there is no blood around see no side of pain
hay no pain seeing no red at all, see no red rain is
coming down red rain"

Alas, I do not get permission to use the song, however, in this game, I am four degrees from JFK. I am three from Lee Harvey Oswald and Fidel Castro, because I am two degrees from the CIA spy Marita Lorenze, as I meet her daughter, who is selling me a travel bag for two upcoming shoots.

'I love docs.' She tells me in solidarity and support of my film. 'They made a doc about my mom, *Dear Fidel*.'

Because of this first documentary, I will have other opportunities to work on film projects, documentaries and features, all about telling the truth of persecution around the world.

I am aware of the privilege and responsibility upon me to bring these stories, and unredeemed bodies to the light. The stories of those forced to choose between a physical life or a spiritual life, like my ancestors in the Spanish Inquisition, like Maria Barbara Carillo who was burned at the stake for heresy. She was executed at the age of 95.

Carillo was sentenced to death for heresy because of 'relapsed' Judaism. She belonged to a large group of people that were forcibly baptized Jews, who were accused of secretly practicing the Jewish religion.

The Christian Crusades, the blood libels, all those who burn for their beliefs, like Mary Easty and the women of Salem in 1692.

Ann Glover an Irish born emigrant to Colonial America, is the last woman hanged for witchcraft in Boston.

Ann Hibbins, the fourth person executed for witchcraft in The Massachusetts Bay Colony, hanged on Boston Common, a place I love to visit as a child, where I feed the ducks. The place where I will meet and later date the Cherokee. The place where I visit with the weeping willows who are weeping this day.

And I will live to forge a path, into a new paradigm that will not demand total sacrifice, that will not engulf the good with equal measures of evil.

Joan of Arc.

Falun Gong.

Backwards world.

CHAPTER NINE

losing north

In the backwards world, newly hatched baby turtles run away from the ocean that is calling them home.

I work at a flower essence store on Abbot Kinney Street, using a pendulum and nature's intelligence to pick the right remedy for those who come in, acutely aware that everyone is a baby turtle, lost, going backwards.

These elixirs have no scent, but are imprints of the energetic vibration of an organic substance that can balance out the energies of the person taking them.

Here, I am initiated. Here, I develop what some would call psychic skills.

I'm usually accurate in my recommendations. One day,

however, a man with athletic build walks into the store and asks for my assistance.

I choose a remedy for him off the shelf using the 'sense' I learn to trust, without knowing anything about this particular remedy. I hand him the description of the essence from a corresponding book. He slams the book down and storms out.

'Hmm, That's unusual. I'm not usually wrong about these things.' I am looking at the description of the essence I had offered him and read, 'For someone in denial.'

This is a way to help direct people to their north, their intended career, person, or place they need to go.

Maybe I will find my way home too.

In doing this work, many questions percolate, almost to obsession. What is a soul mate? Why would spirits tell me that someone is a soul mate when the connection blows like the fuse in my one hundred year old apartment?

I am determined to unravel these mysteries before they unravel me.

I don't remember where or when, I first hear a report on the plight of baby turtles who are mysteriously going in the wrong direction- unwitting suicide.

The story never leaves me.
I am a baby turtle.

I learn that the female turtle comes up on shore and lays her eggs in the sand. They incubate, hatch and the fledglings should scurry quickly into the ocean avoiding predators eager to eat them.

In recent years, however, turtles go in the opposite direction of the ocean, threatening the turtle population into extinction.

Like a baby turtle, I fear I have lost my instincts too.

Eventually, I will realize it is not a personal matter.
All of humanity is lost and scurrying in the opposite direction of life.

'Choose Life.' Says Deuteronomy.

According to researchers, turtles should be attracted to the glimmering ripples of celestial light on the water, drawing them to 'return home.'

Car and city lights, however, trick and attract the turtles as they march off into the traffic, parking lots, and into the beaks and claws of eager predators- a certain demise.

Humans all want and need the same things- to be nurtured, fed, and sustained by meaningful work, recognized for our talents and gifts, to be cherished by loved ones, and to be able to contribute to a community. But we, like the fledglings, go towards the trickering flickering false lights of power, fame, money, appearances.

) ((●)) (

I begin writing *Losing North.*

) ((●)) (

Some days, I am a woman walking along the beach like a heroine along a windy bluff, wearing a dark cape against the howling winds in some imagined European film. But my deliverance will be realized in Venice Beach, and I will be wearing cut-offs and a sleeveless red hoodie, needing no thing and no one, enraptured by freedom, simplicity, knowing deeply yet thinking of nothing.

Other days, I am tortured. An endless grief that taunts and berates, a revisiting demon. These could be days of mourning that only a faithful dog and faith itself could assuage over time.

A karmic debt, a lesson?
One flower essence offered at the store is called Love-Lies-Bleeding:

Alleviates Intense Emotional Pain. Aids ability to move beyond personal pain, suffering and mental anguish, transform personal vision, compassionate acceptance of karma. Treats intense pain due to isolation and over-personalization of one's pain.

I buy black dye and begin dying everything.

Some things turn navy, others mulberry or plum. The act of renewal and reinvention appeals in the dead of night.

I also get facile and free with scissors, cutting clothes for quick tailoring and alterations, cutting my own hair, with varied results, and cutting out everything superfluous. Scraps of cloth and hair littered about.

During a visit with a holistic healer who employs metaphysics in his practice, I request, 'Please check, I think there is a curse on me.'

He smile-smirk humors me. But, while on his examination table, he is surprised to confirm that his diagnostic instruments and techniques reveal that in fact *I am* riddled with curses. Curses that thwart any romantic union. Curious! He sets out to eliminate them, but can't. Like most healers, he has his own.

It seems that the spell cast on me is that men will be attracted to me, state that they love me, but, I will not be invited to dwell in Love's shelter because they will not act on or claim that love, and I will never quite understand why.

It seems that men will 'love' me, but will not want to be in a 'relationship' , a word clouded in a heavy condensation of sentimental semantics, like the densest of fogs that roll off the Grand Banks of Newfoundland. Because after all, 'We already are in a relationship.' They say.

Perhaps they have other girlfriends 'for the sake of convenience,' and so forth, or because they 'don't want to hurt me', or because they are too busy for a relationship, until they end up with a girlfriend.

'He's just not that into you.' Says the book. That is actually its title.

Yeah, yeah.

I want to understand.

Is this what my true self wants? Will I be more productive, balanced, happier alone. Am I built like a surfboard going it solo on a wave, or am I a bicycle built for two?

I fear I have lost my instincts, like the baby turtles, lured by the false lights and illusions.

) ((●)) (

Being 'in love' versus love:

In Weight of Light, Neshikael tells Ani-

SHIKA
Please try to remember, you want to 'be in love' but you are in love. It's all perfect.

ANI
Perfect? Easy for you to say, you're outside all of this.

I'm here!

SHIKA
It's perfect. Ani, it is perfect.

ANI
Not for me it isn't...

) ((●)) (

Is being 'in love' a tipping point, a caveat, a matter of level or incline, or a separate and parallel track? What is its shape?

Is this something we are imprinted for like some spiritual DNA, or coded in the heart, informing the biology to send off chemicals that will act to ensure and reinforce the predestined connection?

Is it similar to distinguishing merely *hot* from *boiling water*?

Is there an equation, a quantifiable qualification, a calculation?

Can it be measured like IQ, separating and distinguishing the average, from the smart, and smart from genius.

I have heard it compared to the acceleration of the golden ratio- if their ratio is the same as the ratio of their sum, to the larger of the two quantities?

Or is it like a cervix which must be dilated ten centimeters before a birth can safely occur, viability, like the number of months a fetus can survive outside the womb?

Is this love viable? Will his heart open to ten centimeters to birth this love, or just another still born?

My name which means 'mistress of the sea,' has me contemplating a return to the bottom of the ocean. But I am not sure my webbed sisters are happy there either, so perhaps my home is elsewhere.

To fill in gaps of comprehension, I conjure or remember stories, of what I might have done to create this situation that makes my spirit hemorrhage. I speculate stories to fill in the missing pieces, like the ancient Biblical art form of Midrash, to explain the spell that I am under. Asunder.

Midrash 2:
I am his mother in a previous life who abandoned her

son. So in this life, Finn withholds, though my love for him is without condition or limit, desiring only to console and comfort, support. I must endure his distancing and earn his trust again.

Or
Midrash 3:
I am a general, who, out of selfish motivations, sends my troops, young, healthy men, into a battle that will result in a certain massacre.

In this life, they all come back to me from all corners of the world, shattered to their core from violence and war, that I must pay for in the privacy of vulnerability, at the hands and heart of their darkened-ness, by their detachment and addictions- porn in place of intimacy, drugs and spirits replacing their own dimmed spirits, and other devastating symptoms of post-present traumatic stress dis/order.

Years later, while facing westward during the ocean's high tide, mid-day, mid-life, I understand that I can be neither abuser nor victim to the evil that destroys men and subsequently women, separating them from themselves and from their lovers, but must use spiritual warfare to destroy the demons of war and porn.

Now is the time for that sword from the other dimension.

Eden is Burning.

In my thirties, versed in the New Age methodology of manifestation, I purchase a notebook on Main Street and find a nice corner seat to write the Universe a letter asking for my *leib-shein,* soul mate, blue flame, *b'shert*. Whatever.

Minutes later, a young, colorfully dressed man strolls past me, comes over and sits next to me,

'I'm here.' He announces.

'I'm here. Show me what you just wrote?'

'I can't show you.' Furrowed brow, nervous giggle.

'Well, I'm here.'

'I hope he likes dogs.' I think.
He, in a short time, however, will prove a most unsavory individual and this occurrence will send me on a quest.

At seven, I have a harem costume made of ivory silk from my aunt's wedding dress, kept as a secret treasure

in an old torn blue suitcase under my bed. I make a proper genie bottle from the identically shaped empty Sabra Liquor bottle that I wrap in tin foil, emulating Genie, my favorite TV show, imagining I that I am her.

I have a dream as a little girl that allows me to say in truth that 'I Dream of Genie' - I blink and make my white and blue trimmed desk drawers that my mother had painted, open and close. But that is the zenith of my magic powers. Frustration.

I'm only a baby wizard, junior genie, demi god.
This deep desire for a mystic's life seems quite incongruous in my suburban New Jersey childhood of strip malls and more malls.

In the study of my father's colleague, I find a book, 'Jewish Magic and Superstition: A Study in Folk Religion.' Printed in 1939.

'Can I borrow this?' I ask on a visit.

He laughs, 'Why would you be interested in that?'

Eventually, I paint a series of acrylic and mixed media paintings on large glossy paper, based on the symbols and incantations from the scholarship of this book. Of course!

As a young woman, it seems obvious to me that the split between cerebral, law based, Judaism and its

Hasidic experientially heart based counterpart, is a divorce which has left the children bereft. Because, laws without deep understanding of spiritual meaning are hollow and without form. Conversely, *heart* without form is content without grounding, lacking application.

When I head off to rabbinic school, I suspect that this could herald opportunities to bring the estranged schools of *Hasidim* and *Mitnagdim*, heart and mind, content and form, together again. But, as a rabbi, I will forever negotiate, compromise, justify, and live fragmented in the realm of duality.

The rabbi is the center of the community, both scrutinized and esteemed, while the artist remains forever outside, observing, commenting. Tolerated, but, only respected if substantial income and celebrity is amassed.

I am visiting my parents during a vacation from rabbinical school. In the car, my parents are bickering in their usual blame game way, arguing about who made the other one late.

'Do you know, I am both of you, and this warring goes on inside me all the time.' I state.

'I'm sorry,' acknowledges my surprised artist, mother sympathetically. My rabbi father pays attention to the road ahead.

) ((●)) (

As I fumble my way through a 'new age' supernatural haze, I wonder if I am just an underachieving manifester. Or is there a bigger concept that I'm supposed to get here?

Manifesting is not a trick like top hat rabbit retrievals. Nor is it proof of one's providential prowess, like producing the biggest ocean front home, the hottest mate, the most resource depleting vehicle.

Because now you have a rabbit, or two or three, or a behemoth of a car.

What will you do with your white furred herbivores?

I become aware of how belief systems have been twisted and warped to support self-indulgence. Fulfilling 'desire' seems a way to lubricate the market place while feeling holy all the while. Monitize, canonize, comprimise, catatonic consumerism.

Uh oh.
In a TV add, a perky young brunette breaks a heel while crossing the street, but, because she has this plastic card she replaces her shoes effortlessly. But wait, now she can a get a dress to match! And while she is at

it, why not get the hair and nails done too. Yes, it's all possible-all in your desirous right. Just 'manifest'!

The ad ends here. We don't see the moment when the bill arrives, the sick look on her face, the extra hours she will have to work to pay this off, the sacrifice that must be endured.

True spiritual enterprise requires using such powers well- not wasting them on filling the 'self' with a temporary appeasement of the emptiness or feelings of 'lack,' because true spiritual enterprise espouses that this state is only illusory in the first place.

Rather than seeking to fill the pit, I learn that the pit is only an underground well, a wellspring and source of life, not a closet.

'What's so bad about lack? ' My friend KC asks.

I quiet myself to listen and receive a response to this 'insatiable' mentality.
'Well, it's a lie.' The answer comes.

I envision a tree whose leaves have fallen off. What if the tree got upset because it was losing its leaves, and tried to hold on to the falling ones, or take leaves from another tree? That would not allow for its natural cycle, the blooming and budding in tune with the rain and sun. If all of the trees and all of nature reacted to emptiness and loss this way, we would be in big trouble.

We can't be afraid of the bare seasons, the barren, and hollow, are after all, just a season, a cycle, the process.

So, manifesters, beware, know the fine print. There is always a price to pay, every choice has a consequence. No loss no gain.

As my *Bubbe*, Gert, in heavy Yiddish accent would often say, 'For nothing you get nothing.'

A sacrifice, an exchange.

The Chinese practice of Wu Wei is accepting the things that come naturally, without force or manipulation.

Like all the pets that show up in my life.

) ((●)) (

Juno, born under a sink in a Harvard Square studio, mothered by a squatting stray mama cat that needed a home, is a fluffy calico, black white and golden brown. She is very cat and very much my cat.
When I leave for California I give the cats, Lilli and Juno, to LJ.

W doesn't want Lily, *his* cat.
LJ will pass Juno onto a friend who has a farm in

Connecticut. She is eaten by coyotes, he later tells me over the phone. LJ had Lilli 'fixed' and she nearly dies. She was never the same.

The bad news -
If the cat represents me or my female nature, I am vulnerable, ravaged, unprotected by the very men who should be protecting.

Good news -
The ancients believed that animals could be sacrificed on our behalf. Juno's life is taken which reminds me that I had escaped, but they were casualties. We don't all survive. She is sacrificed for my freedom.

And I am free.
Sort of.

According to Roman mythology, Juno is the protector of women and of marriage. Goodbye sweet, fickle, Juno cat.

I've had as many pets come through my life, as I have people. My subsequent pets will, serendipitously, find their way to me, and like foster children, like W and the Cherokee, will eventually get passed on to their final destination.

) ((●)) (

My first apartment was in Boston, in Kenmore square. I share with Emma who is a student at Emerson, a Scorpio. She is dating Rick, a Cancerian, two floors up, also studying at BU.

I have a cerulean blue parakeet that I purchase in Central Square named Candide, after the book I don't read by Voltaire.

Emma makes the poor judgment of taking care of a friend's cat and bringing it to our place, forgetting the food chain's link and order.

I return home from school one evening, there is a note on the front door pleading for me not to enter. When I'm finally given permission to come in, I find blue and yellow feathers everywhere. Emma, who has dispensed of the tiny de-plumed body, apologizes profusely. I am sullen.

Lily was rescued from the snow banks of Vermont while we are staying with friends for the holidays. W goes out for a walk where he finds what looks like a stick poking out of the snow. Reaching for the stick, he discovers it is attached to a cat, this is her frozen gray speckled and striped tail!

She is his cat and quite like him in fundamental ways. Her past leaves her untrusting, skittish, aggressive. She attempts to get close to me by jumping onto my shoulder from behind, digging all her claws into my back to hang on. Stunned and pained, I will react with great force, hurling her across the room. This routine does nothing to engender trust or affection in either direction.

Wounds are reinforced, claws on skin, karma on karma.

Kelev, the family dog I grow up with, dutifully endures my Good & Plenty pink manicures and being stuffed into ski pants. The matted black mid- size pooch is a patient and forgiving pet with a penchant of eating my Crayola crayons that makes her poop rainbows.

Krya, the cockatiel, has flown into the window of the couple sitting across from me at a Berkley dinner party who convey that the bird is unhappy living in their laundry hamper.

'I'll take it.' I volunteer, as I have a beautiful vintage

wrought iron birdcage, a farewell present from a neighbor when I left Boston.

And besides, a feng-shui expert had warned me that having an empty birdcage in my bed room in front of a black and white poster of a woman cropped at the shoulders, seemingly beheaded, would be a disastrous impediment to my 'relationship sector.'

Having moved four times in less than two years, I am missing animal companions.

'My life is so unstable I can't even take care of a pet! My friends have houses and children and I can't even manage a pet!' I repeat to myself relentlessly. After weeks of this esteem-ciphering mantra, I think, 'Well, that's exactly why I need to get one.'

I purchase a worn red leather collar and leash at the thrift store on Main street.

```
Weight of Light

EXT. PIER STREET. DAY
```

On her way home, Ani sees a man by an old rusted station wagon lifting a milk crate out of the back, filled with adorable yelping little puppies. The man is barefoot in hippie-groovster attire.

ANI

Are you giving away these dogs?

DOGOWNER

Yeah dude, the mom is pregnant again, need to get rid of the litter.

He pulls out one of the dogs from his old and dilapidated car and the little tyke licks her face. Ani is delighted.
She whispers in his ear as the dog continues to lick her face.

ANI

Are you my doggy?

She turns to the owner.

ANI

I think he's my dog.

DOG OWNER
I have some string
that you can tie
around his neck till
you get him home.

ANI
Wait , I have a
collar at home. I'll
be right back!

Ani and the puppy walk down the street
together.

I am confused, I thought my perfect pet dog was a black pit bull lab mix, like a dog I knew and loved in Boston, called, Freud. How can his be *the one?* He is a golden Asian mix and looks like a cross between a fox and a polar bear.

But he is so mine.

All my other pets have been foster pets, they came and went, but this one is where I turn the karmic corner, he is for keeps. Zion, my familiar.

) ((●)) (

Then, there is the crisis of animals who are not pets.

I am eating chicken. I'm three. I know the animal names, so I am puzzled. Is this the same 'chicken' from my picture books? I wonder.
'Mom, is this chicken, like a chicken chicken?'
'Yes.' She replies.
'No, really?'
We repeat this with lamb, and fish, but I am very confused about the chocolate mousse. Everyone laughs. I don't know why.

When I am nine, I meet a young woman with long, light brown hair. She is a vegetarian! So, it *is* possible! Now I have proof. Yet, my parents dissuade me from giving up meat nonetheless.

At fourteen, during a family holiday feast, the notion of food stuffed up the rear of a bird, then passed around the table on a china plate for consumption, is the final betrayal of sensitivities to a sentient being.

Meat never passes my lips again.

Do the animals we eat link us to them, becoming part of our genetic structure, imprinting their codes onto us, in the lining of intestines, stomach, esophagus - or imagination?

Will they become part of words we will speak?
Or like native American animal totems, that guide us through life.
Will they haunt or bring awareness?

Like moths, and spiders.
Like baby turtles.

) ((●)) (

Late fall, a spider fashions its web in the corner of the ceiling in the salmon and green tiled Berkeley bathroom. I keep a fierce and suspicious eye on the wee arachnid all winter.

But, by that damp February, she has not caught a single insect. Now I am worrying about the poor creature an-will even try catching her a meal myself.

I begin to understand her in a way I hadn't before. Her ability to create her home from her very body, to weave remarkable webs made of protein rich vitamin K, both durable and beautiful, barely visible in certain light.

She gets a bad rap as a seductress, but in truth, she is a pacifist, receptive and patient, living wue wei really, only taking what comes her way.

The spider totem represents the alchemist balancing opposites - past and future, strength and gentleness, physical and spirit, male and female. She is a symbol of infinite possibilities, of creation, eternally weaving patterns of life and living.

'Those who weave magic with the written word usually have this totem,' I learn, for these are the 'keepers of a primordial alphabet', as I imagine Charlotte suspended in her web of ancient hieroglyphs and Pulitzer Prize worthy pros.

) ((●)) (

But sometimes, the delicate threads that connect us are also knots to untangle. And knots cannot be forced, only gently massaged, patiently loosened.
The knotted lover-friend-entanglements- enstrangel-ments in my heart, like scar tissue, are riddles unsolved. My *Groundhog Day.*
I am stuck in this web, or karmic loop, a synthesized drum machine, delay unit loop- like the walking dead, a ghost, reliving the same day out of time, out of place.

After years of *feng-shui*, Gold's gym, angel guides,

life stream re-threading, reality weaving, positive affirmations, exorcisms, belief removals and the failed curse elimination, not to mention a Master's Degree, the exact same scenario repeats.

Should this be accepted as fate?
What in life can be altered, what cannot be?
Are there consequences to imposing will?

Abraham bargains with God trying to save Sodom and Gomorrah.
Can we negotiate the terms?

And when do desires' negotiations lead to bargaining with the devil?

I remember the ghost of Westminster Ave, stuck in the same day for nearly a century.

I must be able to free myself, like I did him.
And bring the others with me.

It is not uncommon that I sing while walking home from the cafe at two a.m. closing time, when the usually noisy city streets are now my peaceful hamlet.

One song in particular, Joni Mitchell's 'Same Situation'

often leaps to my lips:

'Again and again the same situation
For so many years
Tethered to a ringing telephone
In a room full of mirrors
A pretty girl in your bathroom
Checking out her sex appeal
I asked myself when you said you loved me
Do you think this can be real?'

Sometimes, I sing while walking the dog along the grassy lawns of Ocean Park Avenue in the early morning hours.

Is Pesagniyah, the angel who ushers prayers of grief to heaven, listening then?

'Still I sent up my prayer
Wondering where it had to go
With heaven full of astronauts
And the Lord on death row
While the millions of his lost and lonely ones
Call out and clamor to be found
Caught in their struggle for higher positions
And their search for love that sticks around'
'You've had lots of lovely women
Now you turn your gaze to me
Weighing the beauty and the imperfection
To see if I'm worthy
Like the church

Like a cop
Like a mother
You want me to be truthful
Sometimes you turn it on me like a weapon though
And I need your approval...'

) ((●)) (

Perhaps L'wren was singing the same song, caught in a web of the 'same situation,' a ghost before she was a ghost.

She created a fragrance, but what she really needed was 'Spirit of Hartshorn,' smelling salts, like those my Grandma Syd always carried in a hard blue cosmetic luggage case, filled with anti-anxiety pills and such that I later convert it into my painting case.

L'wren needs her spirit revived.

L'wren Scott

Top notes : wormwood,star anise,
coriander, marigold and
mandarin orange

Heart : tuberose, jasmine,
geranium, curry tree and cloves,

Base notes: patchouli, leather,
musk, amber and moss.

Although L'wren could tailor the most exquisite finery by hand, clothes worn at the White House and Red Carpet, she could not spin a new situation for herself.

She creates things of such beauty, but she can't remember how to weave a beautiful new story.

Aspiring to be,
Equanimous, day to night,
Full moon equinox.

A man named Bird flew into my life one June. He collects and catalogues dying languages. I am a dying - evolving - morphing language. He seems to adore my syntax and how words bubble from my mouth after midnight.

He wants physical tactile certainty. He thinks that means real. I know real could never be seen with the human eye.

He records my language in his mind and then leaves, continuing his search for 'real' experiences on linguistic escapades across the continents, meeting me for a meal when coordinates converge. I return to watching Luna's waning and waxing, and writing haikus.

Retreats, then charges,
My surging heart must learn
to beat with Heaven

) ((●)) (

Documentary Treatment: LOSING NORTH

Like the bees, turtles, and other species, we have lost our basic instincts and are therefore, in a very real and metaphoric sense, compromised in our ability to know and discern good from bad.

Zhang Guolao, one of the Eight Deities from China, rode backward on his donkey. Few people know why. He discovered that going forward, progress, is moving backward, so he rode the donkey the other way around. The documentary, Losing North, asks if and how we as a society have lost our instincts or moral compass, rendering us unable to discern good from bad, beauty from banal, healthy from destructive. Has everything become inverted? Are we going backwards as the ancient Buddhist monk claimed as he rode a donkey backwards to assert this very point?

Why are starving women, who look drug addicted, the ideal of contemporary beauty? Why do we choose them as our 'models'? Why is it that a model's career takes off when she gets cancer and is dying, or that women emulate a plastic Barbie doll?

How did our society come to glorify the underworld with parasitic vampires as 'sexy' heroes, replacing Michelangelo's visions of heavenly scenes? Why is Gap making baby clothes with skull and cross decorations?

Like newly hatched turtles, now threatened by extinction, who lose their sense of direction back to the ocean and instead, follow the 'false' lights of the cities. A suicide, as they are eaten by scavengers, or run over by cars.

The film's content is based on the scientific research of Bruce Lipton, Maryam Henein, George Langworthy - Vanishing of the Bees, Philosopher Roger Scruton, Emperor's New Clothes- Hans Christian Anderson.

The intention of the filmmaker is to investigate, through personal narration, interviews, classic fables, historic and scientific research, the connection between morality and aesthetics.

The film will look at the role of art in society, while examining factors that contribute to the contemporary 'state of art.'

Has 'high art' simply become like Hans Christian Anderson's story of the Emperor's New Clothes, where the emperor and all his subjects are fooled into believing the swindler who convinces them of a garment so fine you can't even see it?

Should we trust the experts and leaders in all fields?

Politics, religious, health care and education, have all been compromised by greed, leading to corruption that is exposed daily, chiseling away at faith in institutions and individuals who have been placed in positions of trust.

The result seems to be a sort of weak 'moral immune system', where people can easily be infected, and further weakened and compromised.

Perhaps the numbers of people on antidepressants and anti anxiety medication are an indication of the consequence for losing one's inner compass, not to mention those self-medicating, with alcohol, drugs, shopping, and TV.

The media, consumerism, food engineering, legal medication- medical industry, have all conspired, either intentionally or not, to trick the individual's system for the purpose of keeping the consumer addicted, rendering most humans too concerned with appeasing their addictions and pleasures to engage in matters of the heart or principle.

The film weaves together a picture of where we are now collectively, while offering alternative examples to move forward, engaging people in an appreciation of fine art, craftsmanship, values of mastery, pride, quality and beauty.

Can art affect our biology?

How does 'bad art' confuse our instincts, and eventually, our sensory perceptions? What happens when we perceive something as ugly, but are told it is valuable? Does the body stop trusting the information it takes in? Is the system breaking down, shutting down?

Shen Yun Performing Arts will be featured as an example. The company seeks to revive the five thousand year-old artistic traditions of China that thrived before suppression from the Chinese communist state. They believe that the grace and beauty of an artist is fundamentally connected to their character. The performers of Shen

Yun practice truth, compassion and tolerance with the same dedication and seriousness as they practice their strict regimen for perfecting bearing and form, honing skill sets such as jumps, turns, and flips, and extremely demanding aerial techniques. The company cultivates both body and heart, with the goal of achieving pure beauty.

It comes as no surprise that the modern day machine, totalitarian, and consumerist corporatocracy, wants to eradicate this thing of beauty. The CCP is now trying to stop their performances worldwide, and severely persecuting these kindhearted people within Mainland China. Backwards?

Flower Essence:
Pencil Cholla Cactus Flower Essence, for finding your way back to your own path - clarity of direction.

CHAPTER TEN

ladders to heaven

uende:

1. A quality of passion or inspiration.
2. A spirit.

Seeking for one seems to bring both.

Committed to painting, I move into in my first live-in art studio, just out of undergrad, twenty-four hundred square feet of windowless basement located on the Blue Line in East Boston. Without windows, time is suspended. Tungsten lights simulate cool blue daylight that I will paint by at all hours. It is here that I first have the idea to create an installation piece, 'Jacob's Ladder.'

Jacob ben Isaac, from the book of Genesis, is on the

run from his avenging brother. He takes a stone for a pillow, and goes to sleep dreaming of a ladder reaching to the heavens. Angels ascend and descend.

'He awakes, surely the Lord is in this place, and I didn't realize.'

It is not until I am in a group show on Boston's Newbury Street years later that I will have the opportunity to actualize the installation.

The seven foot ladder, constructed from tree branches found in Vermont woods, is collaged with handmade paper the color of the changing sky, inscribed with angels' names in gold Hebrew letters.

Michael. Great archangel whose name means 'Who is as God.'
Emmanuel. 'God with us.'
Azrael. Archangel who separates the soul from the body upon death.
Kochabiel. Prince angel of the stars.
Haniel. God's Grace.
Kerubiel. Prince angel of the Cherubim.
Bat Kol. Voice of divine prophecy.

The ladder is suspended from the ceiling, floating about a foot from the hard wooden floor.

Aftiel . The angel of twilight
Raziel. Guards the secrets and sacred mysteries.

Chamuel. Comforter of God, love, compassion, creativity and forgiveness.
Temperance. Angel of the elixir of life.
Muriel. Rules the month of June and is known as the angel of perfume.

Does Muriel too rule June's birthstone, the pearl?
Muriel is busy this day of the opening, my birthday.

I was born on the new moon in June when Jewish and secular calendars coincide, in Turkey, the country where east meets west.

I am in the gallery, across from the Trident Cafe, at the request of Natalia, who has asked me to write about my work, transcribing it on the walls for the show. The writing is composed in the tranquility of the Vermont studio, where I study the bird calls from my feathered neighbors, paying close attention to the opera of communication around me.

But now I am ornery, resenting having to work indoors on my birthday, on this beautiful warm day, a rare phenomenon in Boston.

Then, up on a ladder working on the installation, it occurs to me, that perhaps there is no better way to spend this day than doing and celebrating the work of my life.

On the gallery wall I describe in an allegory, how the

subjects of my paintings, soldier's boots, teacups and roman numerals, are related, as they become animated characters, illustrating the story.

To be Read like Water

This story begins with three angels delivering,
to the tents of Abraham,
the message of life,
and we, like Sarah,
laugh,
skeptical of angels
and of our
birth.
We are in the desert,
there are marks made
in the sand
marking time, marking our
being,
ancient incantations
scripted in Sefat,
We bless the path,
the comings
and the goings
and the clues of the crossing.

We come to a sign 'V' a Roman numeral, five.
One of us says it's the converging
road ahead,
another tells us of its Roman Fiveness
A woman among us recognizes herself here-

the shape of female,
V for vagina.
'And Venus, planet of love and beauty',
adds an astrologer, informing that is the symbol
for fiery Aries,
ruled by Mars
god of blood and battle.

Hearing this, the boots become attentive,
familiar with ways of war
evident by their worn leather
imprints of impasses,
impressions of oppression
we listen to them,
stretching to understand
their travels and trials
and wounds.
note the dark spaces between each heavy heal
creating v for vortex, violence,
vanishing point.

'Enough' protests the teacup.
having no knowledge of points or angles,
for she is round and smooth
and tells only of long
dreamy morning rituals.
Oolong,
jasmine, Rose
hips, deep French Roast,
words of corporal pleasures are
exchanged-

fragrance, warmth, sharing
we gather the given and continue.

The next sign, II, Roman numeral two.
Two people
under one roof
tensions and
tenderness
existing
together
held for eternity
bonded in marriage
observe two lines
angels, trees, outrage legs
the spaces-
contemplation of relationships the dynamics
between cups and boots.

Surely as a journey
is a journey
the III of Abrahams divine
messengers leads us to
the ladder of Jacob's
prophetic dream-
'just tilt your heads to the side' they advise.
We do. we see.
Jacob's dream ladder.

Army boots want
to climb
he wants redemption,

transmutation, ascension from soil, from blood,
grace.

The teacup wants
only to dream;
she knows that dreams
are doorways, more real
than you or I
or the stone which Jacob chose for his
pillow
that prophetic night.

So we fall asleep
like we did at
the foot of mount Sinai
and dream the great dream
visioning the fine threads
connecting all that
is, was, will, be.

Remembering what we
forgot at birth
and will forget again,
that our task and privilege
is in giving significance
and honor to every moment,
and to pass this on
like our names,
from dreamer to daughter,
from seeker to son,
telling the taleof these threads

and the wonderment
of the weaving.

The symbol of the ladder will re-emerge, another opportunity for ascension. But, attachments have to be abandoned, false notions eradicated.

Tonight the moon is full. With Lapsang Souchong at the café, dusk turns to night as summer turns into fall.

Before heading home, I set the time on my phone to include Paris.
Paris time is 5:56 a.m. I wouldn't be there for a number of weeks but my re-memory and compass are now set in the direction of the city of lights.

I had never been to glorious Paris, but the imagined, metaphoric threads connecting me across the Atlantic, beyond time and space, are no less real.

Everything is now recalibrating towards Paris, as I seek out all things French. Lolita Lempicka. Edith Piaf. Agnes Varda. Vannina Vesperini. Perfume, music, film, lingerie, and ghosts, Camille, Renee, Marthe, Rose and Joan of Arc.

It seems, however, that Aurelia Thierree, a performance artist, is not available in Paris. We first meet in Los Angeles.

I am working at a newspaper for the Arts and Entertainment section, covering Aurelia's Los Angeles performance of her one woman show. She will subsequently surface in my musings for various project ideas over the next few years.

Inspiration is an invaluable currency, perhaps the most, more valuable to me than gold, more intoxicating than whisky, more useful than laundry detergent or jumper cables. But, it is a sort of jumper cables, detergent, whisky and gold, combined.

I thirst to be staggered by art, senses besieged, or just infused and saturated by its intangibles.

I am told that I inspire others, and at every opportunity I endeavor to. So when inspiration comes my way, in the form of nature, film, music, image or human, I am enraptured, and exceedingly grateful. Finn is such a human, and Aurelia too.

Epoch Time Article
By Masha Savitz

LOS ANGELES– Sitting in the Freud Playhouse, watching the sensual and evocative images of 'Aurelia's Oratorio' unfold before me, I have the distinct sensation that if this were the entirety of my life and I never left this darkened theater, it would be a good life.

'Aurelia's Oratorio,' is like a beautiful, existential poem; A stylish, funny, and quirky inverted world where kites anchor flying people, clothes wear people, and demons are made of delicate white lace in a dreamscape of imagination.

In one scene, puppets watch a 'human show,' perhaps hinting at greater truths about existence, as the human ultimately controls the puppet audience.

My following thought, 'This is life, and we do in fact live in a reversed world, a circus of the absurd.'

'Sometimes life is more surreal than we would like to admit,' says the charming Aurelia Thierree during a conversation. When asked if she identifies with the main character, Aurelia replies 'When you dream, you adapt to it. While you are dreaming, you don't question it at all, I went with that idea in the show.'

Victoria Thierree Chaplin, Aurelia's mother and daughter of Charlie Chaplin, designed and directed this show with her, even sewing costumes and building props.

'She works instinctively, without any sense of the whole, until at the end things start to place themselves and themes emerge. She has an idea and builds it physically,' says Aurelia of her mother. When asked what its like to work with her, she said, 'exciting, passionate, it is always invigorating to be around that.'

'She has crazy ideas and builds them,' Aurelia laughs, describing the challenges of a particular act in the show involving a model train. 'I never thought it would be possible,' but she attributes the success to her mother's strong conviction and vision.

'It is always good to work with people with common desire and the work becomes most important.

The show has no dialogue, so it travels well.'

Aurelia said that what inspires her is, 'The fragility of the human experience- you never know if it will work, it remains an alive experience.'

No doubt, Aurelia, with the circus in her veins and a heart of grace, does just that.

Yes, life is absurd, but the Thierree-Chaplins make it seem elegant, fantastical, magical. And like the best that art can offer, they remind me to just 'enjoy the show,' to appreciate the fragile and yet enduring nature of the human experience.
I envision Aurelia playing the part of Ani, in Weight of Light.

In our limited conversations, I never mention my Charlie Chaplin connection with the ghost of the Westminster house. Maybe the time would still present itself. Maybe it didn't matter, maybe it did.

Attempting to grasp the essence of things, it is shown to me that a significant aspect of my essential nature is one drawn toward sensuality.

Though reasonable, it seems superficial. Even shallow. Maybe I'm even a little insulted.

I need further explanation, which reveals that sensuality is created by a positive physical experience, evoking an emotional response, which leads to, or induces spiritual awareness.

A cozy arm chair, for example, elicits feelings of comfort and ease, fostering the experience of being safe in the world, held and supported by a benevolent universe. Skin gently stroked with the most gentle of touches, light refracting the billion tiny beads of wet from above on a foggy night that gently moistens your face, are among the innumerable delights that conjure awe and the mysteries of this world. And then, I am appeased.

When I had begun cultivating in Falun Dafa, with the purpose of casting off demon nature, sensuality seemed a vain human trait.

'The middle path' teach the Eastern sages, 'no extremes,' which I, true to my nature, practice, extremely. Always trying to hit the right note, tuning the strings, not too loose, not too tight. Pitch perfect.

Many moons pass during which I wear the simplest attire, minimalist silk tunic, leggings, boots, balancing appropriateness, function, and aesthetics with the intention of non-attachment.

But one person's vanity is another's sacred right.

On the San Francisco subway, coming back from getting a hair cut at Vidal Sassoon near Union Square station, I feel utterly transformed. How is this possible, it is just a haircut?

While riding the train, I consider that all cultures and

religions have very specific rituals and beliefs around hair.

Jewish Orthodox men don't cut their sideburns, women hide their hair under wigs or hats for modesty, Rastas' grow hair in dread locks, Hindus have at times worn their hair in locks, and monks shave to baldness to rid themselves of human attachments.

We westerners, however, relegate hair to the world of fashion and glamour.

On the following visit, I am eager to hear my hair-dresser Raini's, thoughts on ritual, hair and her role in both.

'Are you aware of your ability to transform people, like some urban shaman?' I ask as she combs out my hair in styling preparation.
'Yeah, I actually do have that intention.' Our eyes meet in the wall of mirrors in front of me.
'I am amazed you picked that up.'
'Do all hairdressers feel that way?
She laughs, 'Ha!, Look around - no.'
'Well, how do you know what people need?
'I look at their shoes.'

I strive to distinguish between excessive vanity, and essential beauty. To discern between benedictory sensuality and distracting, selfish indulgence.
But always, perfume. Always perfume.

Black Orchid

Top notes: french jasmine,
black truffle, ylang-ylang, black
currant and citrus.

Heart: orchid, lotus, noir gourmand accord,
black plum

Base: woodsy notes, patchouli and
sandalwood, dark chocolate,
incense, amber, vetiver,vanilla, and balsam.

☽ ◖ (●) ◗ ☾

I buy a used cello. I do not play cello. Nor do I to want to learn. This relationship must be free, tactile, visual, a sensory experience of discovery and play with this sensual instrument.

I have enough money for the cello and to eat a little that week, too, because the owner discounts fifty dollars on account of the bow's poor condition.

Something which had once seemed beyond my grasp, after all, why buy a cello you can't play, is now in my tiny living room. Cello is made in Germany and is warm browns, with marks that reveal a life of service to sound.

I draw the bow over the four strings, that I will soon learn by their alphabetical names. To produce any cello like tones at all, brings the simplest and most inexplicable joy.

Before heading out the door, I set the cello between my knees, and drag the bow across her strings, resting my head against the peg and scroll to feel sound.

One of my favorite paintings at the Getty is the 'The Doctor's Visit,' painted in 1667- an oil on panel, a tiny piece, only seventeen by twelve inches, by Frans van Mieris the Elder.

One must lean in close to the painting in order to properly see what is happening in its intimate interior. We must peek into a little world of mad precision rendering and textures of pale yellow satin cloth.

I visit the Museum of Fine Art in Boston, where the masterpiece 'The Daughters of Edward Boit' hangs, along with another favorite John Singer Sargent gem, 'An Artist in his Studio,' which depicts an artist nearly falling out of the canvas in such a physically cramped bedroom, whilst painting a spacious landscape.

This echoes a truth about artists - often making art

from a tight cramped and dark space, while our consciousness, our hearts, reach out into vast, beautiful, boundless places, places we will all be transported to via imagination and sacrifice.

If I were a painting, perhaps I would be a Singer Sergeant, where objects emerge from a predominant darkness with pristine color, luminosity and fluid dynamic clarity. But more often, I feel like a Nathan Oliveira, a figure containing an energetic storm of color that seemingly defies its surroundings, or suspended as a blurry form in Francesca Woodman's still photography. Still, this is a vast improvement over the times I have felt a De Kooning.

Six degrees - though born and raised in America, Sergeant schools in Paris, befriends Rodin, and paints a forbidding and powerful portrait of his friend and colleague in 1894. This same year Rodin sculpts a bust of Camille.

At the Boston museum, I observe what seems to be a father and his twelve year old son. They are standing before a plain white plywood board that is leaning against a wall. Some kind of exhibit.

The son looks inquisitively towards his dad, who looks blankly back at his progeny. Neither can work out what this piece is about.

I am angry that this father is made to feel inadequate in

responding to his son, or shame for not understanding the artistic merits of this piece that, in my estimation, is crap.

'Art once made a cult of beauty,' he says, 'Now, we have a cult of ugliness instead. This has made art into an elaborate joke, one which by now has ceased to be funny.' Philosopher Roger Scruton speaks to the feelings of my mind in his documentary, *Beauty Matters.*

'It is not just a subjective thing but a universal need of human beings,' Scruton continues, 'If we ignore this need we find ourselves in a spiritual desert.'

These feelings are roused during my first womens only group art show in Boston. This exhibition indeed leaves me feeling that I am in a spiritual dessert. Upon leaving the show, the Cherokee boyfriend suggests that I must be excited and proud. On the contrary, I explain, I am not happy to be associated with this chaotic, hostile work. It feels like art therapy, sans the art.

This will inform my future work. At least I know what I do not want to make or become.

Finn and I, often while walking my dog Zion on the Venice boardwalk, discuss or debate definitions of art -then attempt to characterize, 'good art.'

Sometimes at this hour, the moon hangs directly over

the Pacific, and the water below, in loving response, glows a pathway of light.

Finn and I agree on this: Art distills, frames, communicates, captures, elevates, and sparks.
Challenges, provokes. Inspires.

We are walking through a rainstorm, thunderous waves pound the shore.

I share with him a dream I have years earlier in my Berkeley bed. My hope is that, he who relishes rational discourse and prizes evidence, my beloved Apollo rolling a cigarette in the rain, might more deeply under stand the one who builds ladders to heaven from twigs, paper, pigment, and wish.

The dream is set at nighttime. I am walking in a forest clearing when something falls onto my head. I realize that it's the moon, which has fallen out of the sky. It hits the ground, cracking open like an egg, revealing a structure made of chicken wire and newspaper like a paper maché high school play prop.

This initially delights me, 'What amazing auspicious luck, to be hit by the moon!' But the feeling turns quickly to a terrible realization - there is no more moon in the sky for lovers and poets to gaze upon.

I am determined that, somehow, I must get the broken and hollow moon back into the sky.

Children appear and begin to jump on the moon. Alarmed I shout,
'No, stop! We need to get the moon back in the sky!'

'Love it,' says Finn, 'That's a great dream. I would help you get the moon back in the sky.'

'Please do', I think.
Yes. Please do.

) ((●)) (

With four planets ruled by the moon, I am particularly stirred by Luna's lure and lore, like the ancient cultures that called pearls, "teardrops of the moon."

Clair de Lune, a poem written by Paul Verlaine in 1869, that translates to The Moon's Light, will later inspire Claude Debussy to compose the famous piano music.

But, what inspires Verlaine? A performance by masqueraders?
Or was the Angel Cassiel, guardian of the moon, karma and time, whispering in his ear?

Clair de Lune

Your soul is a chosen landscape,
Where charming masqueraders,
and bergamaskers go playing the lute

and dancing and almost,
Sad beneath their fanciful disguises.

All sing in a minor key,
Of victorious love and the opportune life,
They do not seem to believe in their happiness
And their song mingles with the moonlight,

With the still moonlight, sad and beautiful,
That sets the birds dreaming in the trees
And the fountains sobbing in ecstasy,
The tall slender fountains
among marble statues.

When Debussy put to music his wistful piano rendition of the poem by the same name, Clair de Lune, the third movement of the Suite 'Bergamasque,' was he thinking of Camille, the sculptress and her emotive marble statues? Did she embody the 'sad and beautiful' with her fierce Sagittarian fire, burning in flames that never let her surrender?

If only she had been born ten days later, like Finn, indestructible. Mostly.

Camille is susceptible to demons, as are many of us. And so too, am I. The demon makes me doubt, makes me believe I no longer want to live in this world. The demon makes me believe for so many years that I am deeply flawed by my undesirability.

Ich - Du.

When do I get my Du?

The demon's lies put me out of harmony with the universe, which is truthful by nature, therefore aligning with lies puts me in opposition of its wonderment, its pure potentiality. Instead, I am cast out of grace, shivering and miniscule in the vastness. The Asura demons, that feed off peoples' emotions, feast on me. I become increasingly weak.

'Choose life.' Says Deuteronomy.

I ask a Buddhist acquaintance, who would later write a 3D horror film, how to get rid of this Karma. He laughs heartily, 'That's the thing about karma, sometimes ya just gotta accept it.'

'Unacceptable. That's UN-AC-CEP-TA-BLE !' I protest. He laughs.

This could not be possible. But, It was.

Punishment or protection? Or the agenda of a higher self, guiding this voyage? All, to one day embrace my once prized, then dreaded, and later cherished, sovereignty.

At the same time, the wonderful contradiction - the more one surrenders to karma, the less tightly one is held in its grip.

The one thing I can recall from a swimming class I took at summer camp makes its way into *Weight of Light*:

```
Footage of an old swimming instructional
video.

Title card says:
What to do if you are caught in
seaweed.

                NARRATOR
        Do not resist because
        you will only become
        more entangled,
        and risk drowning.
        Instead relax your
        limbs and you will
        become freed easily
        and be able swim to
        safety.

Old instructional sepia footage mixed
with beautiful underwater shots of
woman freeing herself from seaweed.
```

At some point I think that perhaps I can handle a solo existence better than most, and that is perhaps why it is ordained for me. Later however, I reconsider this position.

Observing friends like Sila, in a different but committed relationship every two years, it would seem that some people are like a great pair of jeans, that go well with everything. I, on the other foot or hand, seem to be a pair of thigh high snakeskin platform boots. I would take a particular matching.

Perhaps my spirit's evolution is to deeply appreciate life on its own terms - a life of loving all humans, not just focused on one - a life dedicated to higher principles.

) ((●)) (

Am I, in fact, perpetually in the same situation, like Joni's song, or are things changing, both subtly and profoundly, though imperceptibly?

) ((●)) (

On a bus ride in Northern California, looking out at the Santa Rosa mountains, having recently left my husband, studio, paintings, and job behind, I have an epiphany of sorts:

Maybe I am a failure and will have nothing in this life,

or, maybe I am destined for greatness.
But this is not the epiphany.

The realization was, that in either case, I would have to live exactly the same way- humbly stumbling towards authentic expression and spirit.

It seems that I can, through rigorous cultivation, defy old forces, dissolve old karma, transcend the human condition, find a renewal of faith that I might wake from *Groundhog Day.*

Maybe awake, with all of humanity leaping into a technicolor blaze of special effects.

Crony Amil, decrees for the thousandth time, that he wants 'a hot girl. Ya know, skinny and blonde - ya know, hot.' Sable maned, sometimes temperate, sometimes feverish me, is irritated and exacerbated.

It isn't just Amil, but the circumference of the world that challenges my sensibility, with particularly narrow definitions of 'beauty', an affront and imposition to all things I value and believe in.

) ◖ (●) ◗ (

My thoughts return to the series of intercourse paintings I made called Come/Union. They were prayers for balance, harmony and integration between male and female, yin and yang, depicted by epic sized genitals during intercourse, penetration, connected as one flesh, or two symphonious parts.

I beseech you, Rachiel, ruling angel of Venus who governs sexuality, 'help me, here.'

'You can't paint these.' Says the fitness-trainer-photographer I am dating. He can't reconcile my intercourse paintings with my rabbinical course work.

But I have. Therefore I can.

A celebrated musician friend, whom I adore for generosity of spirit, is fascinated, albeit, slightly disturbed by this body of work, the current subject matter.

'Well, some people might wonder about someone who paints sex. That maybe they have some kind of sexual issues.' He suggests or implies as I sit on the peach brocade couch I had procured from the alley.

'If I paint landscapes, would you think I was agoraphobic?' I retort.

He calls some months later to wish me a happy holiday.
'I'm surprised to hear from you.' I say.
'Well, some people make a big impression on you.'

'Will I see you again?
'I don't know.'

BLOOD OF EDEN

INT. UPSCALE WINE BAR. NIGHT

Margaritas at a dimly lit table where Maggie and Lizzie are getting drunk as the bottles collect.

LIZZI

Maggie, they are like sexual Rorschach tests, everyone projects their own attitudes about sex onto the work.

MAGGIE

I know! I intentionally paint each one without gestures, faces and expression, for the very intention to take away all of the

sexy paraphernalia,
you don't know if
they are making a
baby or if it's a
rape, I mean there
are no garter belts,
no red finger nails,
we might consider
this one truth of
humankind that has
made everyone lose
their minds.

LIZZIE

What has happened
to this world?
(slams on the table
dramaticaly)
We are worse than the
animal kingdom. We
have sex for revenge,
manipulation, fear,
to get a job, to
impress friends, to
affirm prowess- it
rules us, it is the
undercurrent and
obsession of this
society
(she slams again)
It's the pretext,

the context and the
subtext!

Wine is refilled, they are now totally
hammered.

MAGGIE
In the war between
men and women, sex
has become the field
strategy, the battle
cry, it's the way
to punish the enemy
by either retreating
or as a weapon in
aggressive attack,
and of course, it
is the victory
celebration!

Arms are waving, glasses clanking.

LIZZIE
Its everyone's
goal, the cause of
every problem and
everyone's solution,
for lack of love, or
esteem, attention,
wanting a child,
feeling too masculine

```
or feminine or not
enough, and for those
who have had it used
as a weapon, it's
the cause of every
pain...
```

Both sip their wine silently with a far off gaze.

I refuse to call my work erotica. It is figurative, or a still life. I decide that as long as I can pay my rent, I can afford to be principled in this regard.

I run out of money, however, and agree to be part of the Erotic Show at the Bellagio Hotel in Vegas.

The curator, a stout, bearded man, tells me that my work is the most honest work in the exhibit. Yes, the antitheses of fantasy- not intended to arouse or tantalize, as everything erotic is eliminated.

In the lobby of the hotel, I meet a contortionist who I will later see again on the Venice boardwalk. He invites me out, but it seems like a punch line to a joke. So I pass on what might have been a good story. Sorry.

In retrospect, I was not sure I could hold to the ideal, calling the work erotica. But I was wrong. I could. I can. You can. We have to.

I later destroy all but one COME/UNION painting. Although my intentions were good, the paintings backfire.

'Call them anything but porn.' I lament.

I cannot bear adding to what is already a downslide of humanity- a malignancy, infectious epidemic against affection, canker of authentic connection.

Some women believe that they now have power because they can objectify themselves, confusing this with freedom or power- A colossal travesty, one of Satan's clever maneuvers, a conniving ploy that is working ingeniously. Satan has a brilliant marketing team.

As a girl, like most girls, I wonder if I'm pretty, or pretty enough.

A thought answers, telling me that if I am a good person, it will all work out. Just do the right thing.

If I evaluate my worth by what I have, I always feel

poor. When measured by what I give, I am rich!
This is great comfort through adolescence and my twenties.
I'm not self-conscience like my fellow sisters, I am unburdened from the self scrutiny others suffer. Even when I am uncertain and clumsy, I am full of self-acceptance, committed to doing the right things-integrity.

'It will all work out, just do the right thing,' I remind myself.

But it is not working out. Has it ever worked out?
I feel betrayed.

I will grow to feel 'never good enough,' for the collective him, the specific him. Surely, I will succumb, eventually, like most females in this culture's climate, this foreboding climate change, to scrutinize, minimize, and despise, every part of a perfect self.

We fell from the garden, consequences of a woman who listened to snakes. The snakes are still here. Now we are blemished and brutalized by insecurity and vanity- victims.

Insecurity, this virus, could leap out anytime and thrash me like a feral cat.

Not crazy enough, but too eccentric.
Not weak enough, but too independent.

Not accessible enough, but too available.
Not smart enough, but too cerebral.
Not beautiful enough, not beautiful enough.

When the musician breaks my faith, that doing the right thing is enough, the faith ruptures like an appendix sending a poison of despair through my system.

A situation that can be fatal.

CHAPTER ELEVEN

disappearing gifts

At times I am bereft of words. Painting is my first language, I say.

I emerge from the sensual, wordless world of images, scent, sounds, metaphors, symbols- the impression.

Words have to gestate inside of me. Or sometimes I go catch them like fireflies that light up in my palm. Or I wrangle words like wild horses, that I will harness, tame, and ride.

Sometimes words must be painfully extracted like a biopsy, observed and analyzed, placed in a petri dish, to see what might grow.

But I learn to construct bridges made of letters that form words, that cross over to the place of people where I might be adept, effective in expressing ideas and feelings. Always a bit of an experiment.

Like most things in this anemic society, however, words are beginning to lose their intrinsic value.

Much like the value of a painting, value is a convoluted creation - a matter of getting as much as possible for as little as possible.

Love, too, is a word with no real worth. Like the federal reserves and treasury bonds, the word 'love' has nothing tangible to back it up.

Monopoly money. Games with the objective of winning.

Like a fleeting appetite, diminishing. Maximum gain for minimum effort. Now that doesn't seem very loving.

I struggle to understand what value someone professing, claiming to love me, really has.
What do these words mean?

On this night, under a change in the weather to warming Santa Ana winds, I reboot my system through a colossal surge of productivity. Again, eager to align, engage with the truth of my nature, honoring its rhythm and pitch. So, I sit at the cafe, feeling more at ease as the sun has set behind the Pacific and twilight rolls into night.

I can feel into the emptiness and the desolation, knowing no one in the human world will comfort.

I am tempted to conjure one from the spirit realm.

I would have to, of course, straddle worlds-

> Conscientiousness, real as me,
> Stretches across time,
> To hold you as real.

Screenplay:
WEIGHT OF LIGHT

Genre:
Fantasy/Drama/Coming of Age

Log Line:
A young bohemian woman, discouraged by the state of human love here on earth, finds herself in a romantic relationship with a spirit, only to discover, that she can't take her human notions about sentimentality to Heaven.

Summary:
Anushka, a young artist, after a series of futureless relationships and the death of her brother, seeks solace in a local bar. She meets someone who doesn't seem 'from here', and finds herself on a strange escapade to understand what is 'real' and what is illusion in matters of intimacy, love, and the heart.

There is a man.
I love (respect, admire, and cherish) him, tenderly and utterly.

We are Kings of Hearts. (Albeit, perhaps with a murmur)

We have known each other many years. During this time, our friendship bears added elements of sexual desire (his), romantic tendencies (mine), other relationships (his), celibacy (mine), and professional collaboration (ours).

Intent on avoiding any Yang complications, I gain thirty-five pounds. It seems a certain foil. But, it doesn't work. Despite the fact that I try to remove myself from entanglements, unfettered by infatuation, we tangle.

Finn is a marksman wordsmith. His words are like confetti, like paint, tear gas, fertilizer, rain, wind - dew, petals and blood. Like bait and hook, reeling me in when we are both vulnerable.

I am weak to his dominance, and to his weakness, to his kingly heart, to his mad sweet utterings. I hate being weak.

He tosses me back into the sea and heads for shore. He has no words for me then.

Until the next time I struggle on the hook.

And so is my ambivalent relationship to words, to freedom and love, when love can be incarceration and freedom, solitary confinement.

Affection, attraction. Ardor.
Alienation.

Anointed in warm bath waters and Dead Sea salt scrubs, I yearn to express and exchange in non-verbal and verbal ways, to give form to the formless and to set other forms free. But rules of entanglement dictate the rules of engagement in matters of endearment.

I never want to choose between freedom and love, so life chooses for me.

In the duality realm, the old paradigms, Joan of Arc must choose life or faith, integrity or death. I have no regrets for my choices and decisions, but things I cannot choose cause sorrow.

I am free and unencumbered, with a rented apartment but no home, a bed for dreaming, a bathtub for visioning, a view of the Pacific for expansion.

I vowed years earlier to use my freedom well.

I keep my vow.

) ((●)) (

To console me the night he inadvertently mentions he has a girlfriend, only after he has slept with me, Finn explains how we are shepherds, and the rest are sheep.

You choose to sleep with sheep, I think to myself, but I choose to sleep with Gods. And I will become one.

I know he too is a God and we can create new worlds, like we had done before. But, he no longer has faith in Gods, so maybe he can not find faith in himself or in me, or in my love. I wish I could use supernatural powers to influence fate, invoke the angel Miniel, who invokes love, but integrity does not permit. All I can do is love and hope to induce re-memory, but I too suffer from occasional bouts of celestial amnesia, and like Tinkerbell, become diaphanous with doubt.

Ever fading.

Time to re-paradigm.

When Finn and I first meet, I decorate a music box for him, painting it the first blush of twilight, with a glazed monarch butterfly wing that was saved with other treasures in tin boxes, ceramic cups, china bowls.

He becomes cross.

'I told you, I don't want things. I don't have room for this!'
'Then toss it into the ocean,' I suggest.

'Then I'm an asshole, what kind of asshole throws out something so beautiful?'

For Finn, gifts take up physical space, but moreover, mind space, a burden of obligation, reciprocation, causing a constellation of upset.

I apologize at the cafe, and thank him for this well learned lesson in giving and in true caring.

Medieval Spanish superstar philosopher Maimonides agrees. This preeminent Jewish scholar, philosopher, astronomer and physician, writes that one of the highest forms of giving is when the recipient does not know from whom he receives.

Leaning on a car meter, in the late hours, Finn expounds on this topic saying, 'One should give according to the other's ability to receive.'

Yes. Agreed.

He too is a philosopher, or 'hears' Sabatiel, angel of intelligence, communicator of divine light.

I had made the music box because it pleased me to create it and to create it for him, it didn't, however, respect and honor his boundary sensibilities.

Benevolence sometimes means retracting, restricting, constricting, forbearing - something I will need to do a lot of.

I am origami, folding myself into intricate shapes, objects and animals. Even a butterfly. But in becoming smaller, I become larger, potent, like the principal of

Tantric practice which instructs the recycling of the life force back into the system by withholding ejaculation. Buddhism advocates abstinence from sex, and as such, desire is mastered - transcended. Although the artist's life is about expression, learning when and how to restrain and when and how best to express, is the true artistry.

According to Kabbalists, God creates the world by tzim-tzum, restricting to a single point.

I practice becoming a point because I will have worlds to create.

February 6th.
We spend the evening together.
'I am open to you.' I share.

Break in action and tone.

Defensively, he warns, 'You know I am leaving… I can turn off my emotions, you know….'

I turn away.

Finn continues even more prickly, 'I love being with

you, being intimate, but I can leave tomorrow. I have to do what I want to do...'

My back still turned, I steam.
'I'm giving you your Valentine's gift now.' I state.
'I told you I don't want gifts!'
'You don't trust me to give you a gift?'
'No.'
Insult to injury.
'Oh, now you are really getting it!' I answer.
More steam.

I go to retrieve the gift, protected in an old eyeglass case.

'Turn on the night table light.' I instruct.
'Now, read the poem.' I pass him my reading glasses from the night stand, along with each stanza of a poem, separately handwritten on gauzy gossamer Zig Zag rolling paper, decorated with inhalable washes of beet and hibiscus powder in a Valentine pallet.

For my vanishing Valentine, a card that will vanish as he warns he will.

> My love endures,
> but not this note,
> like wind and breath,
> this verse to float.
>
> So as you inspire,

know your heart to feel,
what's gone is here,
and love is real.

For this poem and you,
away to fly,
slan leat, ciao, adieu,
my pearl and fisheye.

'Oh, this is lovely, M, you're a diamond girl, you are.' He embraces me, 'Thank you for my poem and tobacco.'

My heart is a soft oyster submerged in the vasty deep, and he is my vexing, provoking, pearl-inducing, Grain of sand.

Years after the first music box, I later leave him another music box on the glass table along with the meal I have prepared for him. Dolphins are engraved in the Cherry Wood, a note saying, 'Have a listen to the music.' It is Clair de Lune.

Perhaps I will toss it in the ocean.

Expiration Dates.

I enter into this entanglement mindful of endings, like falling in love with someone who is dying, but, it is in his *living*.

Maybe I am dying. Something is. Something will.

Or maybe it's just light turning into shadow.
Or the shadows fading in the light.

But some things are born perfectly to live but a brief moment.

The last Passover with Jeremy, the festival commemorating liberation from Egypt, the narrow place, is spent on a family trip to Aruba. Geckos and tropical breezes abound. My skin turns deep brown.

Down the street from the hotel is a butterfly farm that we will visit.
A tiny patch of Eden.

A creature there in the corner of the netted inclusion, the Atlas Moth, by design will spend three times more in gestation than it will living. It is born without a mouth, as it will not need to eat. You see it only lives a few days. In this time, it will mate and continue its cycle.

We continue certain cycles and patterns, but unlike the animal kingdom, we have the possibility of breaking ours.

The Atlas Moth amends my feelings about short lived lives - perfect and complete.

Not all things are meant for longevity, and this magnificent winged creature teaches and reminds me of things that fly away.

I must remind myself
of wings and perfection
and brevity. And bravery.

) ((●)) (

On Valentine's Day, sitting outside drinking tea, Finn and I talk about God, gods and art for hours, about the particle world and the wave world, finding common language, finding each other. We agree that 'particles' represent the reality that we see and experience, and 'waves', as the subatomic, unseen spiritual world.

I tell him about the fairy or goblin that lands on the studio window in the Vermont woods late at night, the most unusual, terrifying and captivating creature with thick white furry body, and translucent, pale green fay like wings.

I finally learn its name, the Luna Moth, my Luna Moth. Of course!

A few weeks later he tells me about a gift he intended to leave for me.

He finds a beautiful moth outside my door. It doesn't move. He picks it up ever so gently to examine its

lacy wings. Lifting the fragile body he carries it into the house to leave as a gift for me, arranging it in a prominent place for me to see to and be dazzled.
And then it flies out the open window.

'How wonderful.' I exclaim. 'Like my gift for you, that flies away as smoke.'

There was a large envelope marked for 'Camille' in Rodin's desk. But when they opened it after his death, it was empty.

Vanishing gifts.

I try to love, especially those I don't particularly like, or those who don't seem to like me, expressing in duty, loyalty, playfulness, gratitude, and creativity.

I adapt many forms. As female, I can take on the shape of other, like liquid, or the container that holds water - fluid, flexible, elastic, stretching, negative shape, letting go.
I learn the shape of male, direct and directed, focused

in the form of a bullet, torpedo, rocket or hammer. A forest of redwood erected skyward. Impenetrable, solid like diamond.

And too, I learn to disappear, dissolve. Invisible. White noise. Fading to white. Whisper, shhhh.

Not here.

Because butterflies do not cocoon and grow wings.
They liquefy.
Reconstitute.
Transform,
with the same enzymes that are in the human heart.

) ((●)) (

Genetic material restructures, reconstitutes, as sperms breaks through the zone of Pelicida.

Twelve codes from the sperm, twelve codes from the egg. Like tribes, disciples, or zodiac signs.

Ich und Du, the field of potentiality, new life created.

Yahweh creates by speaking this world into existence.

So I string, stroke, and stoke words that articulate and

form delicate gossamer tendrils, helices of pulsating quantum entanglement, connecting he and I- Finn and me, where we existed before, and could again, after flesh, breath, wings and wet.

But soon I will cease indulging in such words altogether. There are conventions to collapse and realities to hurdle, new paragons to pioneer, where one does not have to sacrifice - too much.

Where sacrifice need not be so extreme.

Many sacrifices are made to make Red Reign, I'm aware of the sacrifices. I dress in neutrals, the shape of male, direct and directed to be director. Focused, the form of a torpedo, I cannot jeopardize, the film more important than momentary pleasure - all feelings and attraction are under tight wraps until 'it's a wrap.'

When the movie is out,
my guard is down.
I let him in.

When we first meet, I am abstaining from intimacy. The goal is to return to my true, original self. Reboot the system that is having interfacing issues. If I let go of sexuality, I rationalize, and it is intrinsically part of my essential nature, then I can never really let it go. What is me is me, and if not, be gone! This experiment has profound impact as I detach from the procreation program, break free from biologically driven behavior. No agendas in my exchanges with men, I am not acquiring anything or anyone. And then, the possibility of real intimacy.

I am driven to understand the true nature of things, my destiny, and compelled to explore the truth between us.

What is between Finn and I?
And.

do I have to sacrifice you
for integrity?
must you sacrifice me
for sovereignty?

what needs to die, that this may live?
what little darlings must we give-

because some old god delights
in the slaughtered dove?
I reject his appetite,
say love, just love.

) ((●)) (

Venturing too close to closeness is to be swallowed by

the collective conscious- the romantic relation-ship-wreck of projections, expectations and roles that most mortals can not withstand intact.

One day a terrible windstorm comes upon Santa Monica Bay and the news reports that an experienced sailor has lost his life at sea.

His boat rolls up on the shore in front of my home, and is later dragged across the great width of sand to the edge of the boardwalk where it stands for weeks as a monument - A shipwreck, warning of the tempestuous seas of emotion and the mighty winds of coupling.

'You'll never know how much I love you,' says the musician.

'Why won't I know?' the artist asks, 'why is that?'

A hipster Boston artist who makes elegant designs on canvas, and his hipster girlfriend, with bleached pink hair, share a loft space with a neurotic parrot. The parrot plucks out all of his feathers because of a nervous condition, all the while shrieking and calling, 'I *love* you, I *love* you,' while pacing about in his cage, bell clamoring from his frenetic movements. 'I *love* you, I *love* you', he pecks and pleads.

There was one brief moment, Finn and I are embracing, I am overcome by a most delicate feeling, an awareness so sublime, tender and perfect-

I am his and he is mine.

A momentary truth. A far reaching and lasting truth, or a lie?

I have learned to trust art and her process implicitly. I'm never lead astray when I follow my instincts and her guidance. And I learn to distrust romance with equal conviction. It has always led to the place of shadows.

Are such things concocted by demons just to distract me from my life's path, or is this, in fact, the path? I would still encounter many demons.

I grow up thinking that there are good people and bad people, and if I can only discern, then I'll be safe. But, I grow increasingly disheartened and distrusting by this grave error, the truth I fail to understand - that all humans are combinations of these two elements- fisheyes and pearls, light and darkness, good and evil, it is only a matter of ratio, circumstance, and mastery.

) ((●)) (

Weight of Light

INT. ANI'S APARTMENT. DAY
She tries to paint, but she is very distracted and anxious. She keeps looking at the pendulum sitting on the table. She calls Ajay.

ANI
Hey Ajay, It's Ani. Got another favor to ask you. Do you think you can let him come through you. I don't know if it will work, but I'm desperate.

AJAY
Sure, sounds cool. You buy dinner.

ANI

Mexican?

INT. AJAY'S HOME. EVENING

Ajay and Ani are finishing burritos on the porch of his house.

AJAY

Hmm. Stuffed... OK, I am ready. You?

ANI

Let's do it.

They head into the house. The porch door slams behind them.

INT. AJAY'S HOUSE - NIGHT

They are sitting comfortably on the couch facing each other.

ANI

Shika. Are you here? Can I please talk with you?

Ajay sits upright, his eyes are closed.

AJAY
Ani, he's here.
(Change of inflection and tone)
I'm here.

ANI
Shika, is that you?

AJAY
If you turn the lights down, you will be able to see me.

She adjusts the lights. Ajay's face seems to morph into another's. She studies the morphing face with excitement and shock.

ANI
I see you! I really see you. I have missed you. I don't understand what is happening.

AJAY/SHIKA
I am sorry if this has caused you such distress.

He takes her hand.

ANI

I don't understand
what is going on. Why
didn't you incarnate
like you said?

AJAY/SHIKA

I just can't.
Besides, you and I
already have what
everyone is looking
for. It's perfect the
way it is.
Its just too
complicated.

ANI

What's complicated?
Please, explain this
to me.

AJAY/SHIKA

It is your very
'humanness,' your
human emotions. It
was dangerous for
me to get so close
to it. I took a big
risk finding you, I
have compromised

myself too much
already. Emotion,
sentimentality - it
is an actual physical
substance that can't
exist where I am
from. It will always
keep us apart.

Ani is totally bewildered sitting with her knees pressed up against her chest with arms wrapped around them.

Ajay is becoming increasingly antsy, agitated.

AJAY

Ani, I don't have
much more time
here. Please try to
remember, you want
to 'be in love' but
you are IN LOVE.

Ajay starts to squirm and shake, as if he is shaking Shika out of his body.

Ani gets Ajay something to drink and sits with him while he reintegrates.

INT. ANI'S APARTMENT - LATER THAT

NIGHT
Ani writes in the notebook talking to Shika, as we see her putting all the things associated with him in a small box, a pendulum, the feather, and then the journal itself.

ANI (V.O)
I do not claim to
know the perfection
of things, on
the contrary, in
retrospect one can
say, 'aha,' and
'divine timing.' From
my vantage point,
and from my earthly
perspective, it's
confusion, fantasy,
delusion, and more
confusion. And I am
no less caught up in
the wash cycle than
anyone else. The
'dream of us', is so
grand, so palpable to
me - it's magnificence
has hold
of me. I can conjure
no wish to abandon
it, and yet it seems

I have no other sane
alternative now.

She wraps the box in a gold bow.

ANI
Good bye, for now.

She sits and smokes a cigarette.

Scene 2

INT. ANI'S APARTMENT. DAY

Ani is at her easel, she is painting a romantic image of two lovers.

Many unpleasant feelings rise to the surface. She is a combinations of sad, angry, and longing.

She is painting aggressively, hurling paintbrushes across the room at the painting. The hissing voices seem to come from the images in the painting.

HISSING VOICES (V.O.)
You will never have
love. Love is for
others, not you, you
hideous creature. No

man, and no celestial
being would be with
you. Foolish flesh
female, did you think
an angel would save
you from the wreckage
of relationships on
Earth! HA!

ANI

Hey Wim, I gotta get
out of here. You in?

The dog wags his tail. Ani is walking down the street with Wim. She is passing a synagogue and spontaneously enters.

INT. SYNAGOGUE MAIN OFFICE - DAY

Behind the desk, a middle-aged woman with a strong Brooklyn accent and glasses.

ADMINISTRATOR, MRS. STERN

Hello, can I help
you?

ANI

Can I speak with a
Rabbi?

ADMINISTRATOR MRS. STERN
Do you have an
appointment?

ANI
No, I was just hoping
I could maybe talk to
him, but I can come
back another time.

ADMINISTRATOR, MRS. STERN
Please wait here one
minute.

She gets up from her desk and walks to the Rabbi's office while Ani surveys the office.

ADMINISTRATOR, MRS. STERN
The Rabbi has a
meeting in a few
minutes, but says
he can meet with you
until they come.

ANI
Oh, thanks.

The administrator looks down at Wim, points Ani to the door and extends her arm to take the leash.

INT. RABBI'S OFFICE. DAY

The shelves are filled with books, many very old.

The Rabbi, a portly and kind looking man, stands up to greet Ani from behind his cluttered desk.

He extends his hand to shake hers.

Later, the Rabbi is trying to modulate and contain his shock at her unusual confession.

RABBI

Interesting. Very, very, interesting. I will be honest with you..... There are some troubling elements to this... which make me consider if your 'friend' was perhaps more demon than angel.

Ani winces.

RABBI

In my best understanding, a according to main stream Jewish mysticism, angels do not have physical urges or needs, but are from a most pure realm, or state.At the same time, once made flesh, in our physical and tainted world- they can fall.

Ani is riveted, her expression serious.

RABBI

What became of this 'relationship'?

ANI

He said he would take human form and stay here with me, but he never did.

Rabbi plays with beard, closing his eyes in deep thought for a moment.

RABBI

It seems to me that
even an angel that
falls would have
an inner, or outer
directive, calling
him to return to his
original nature. We
all do.

He shrugs and nods, shuckling, (a rabbinic gesture resembling a rocking motion).

RABBI

That might explain
his sudden change of
plans.

Intercom buzzes.

Rabbi looks at his watch.

RABBI

Ah, the Bat Mitzvah
girl is here-
apparently there is
a big debate with her
mother over what her
daughter will wear to

the Bat Mitzvah.

He stands up and sees Ani to the door.

RABBI

I hope in some small way that this has been helpful.

ANI

Yes Rabbi, thank you so much for your time.

RABBI

Don't be a stranger here, you are always welcome - your friend too.

Rabbi opens the door. Ani passes a petite 13 year-old girl with pink dread locks, heavy eye makeup, and face piercings. Her mother is wearing a perky tennis dress, and has perfectly coiffed dyed blonde hair in a bob.

RABBI

Hello Mrs. Schwartz, Rachel....

No, never normal relationships. Just entanglements-spooky action from a distance, and also from close, very, very close. In fact, intimacy is synonymous with spooky action.

While researching for the screenplay, I find definitions.

'It involves a pair of particles linked by the strange quantum property of entanglement. Entanglement occurs when two particles are so deeply linked that they share the same existence.

Entangled particles can become widely separated in space. But even so, the mathematics implies that a measurement on one immediately influences the other, regardless of the distance between them.'

The afternoon is warm. I look for a piece of music to inspire. The trail leads me to *Flower Duet, Lakmé de Delibes,* sung by Anna Netrebko & Elina Garanca. I listen over and over again with mad delight. I am moved to declare this 'Day of Beauty' and go off to enjoy the sensual would, buying sparkly glass beaded bracelets, colored, rose quartz and smoky gray, and taking in the scent of fragrant potions and candles.

'I have found the most beautiful piece of music.' I tell Finn when I see him later that evening.
'Flower Duet?' He asks matter-of-factly.

Suspiciously dumbfounded I ask. 'How did you know?'
'Well, it's the most beautiful piece of music.'

Spooky action.

) ((●)) (

Robert A. Heinlein, the famed science fiction writer said, , '*A human being should be able to change a diaper, plan an invasion, butcher a hog, conn a ship, design a building, write a sonnet, balance accounts, build a wall, set a bone, comfort the dying, take orders, give orders, cooperate, act alone, solve equations, analyze a new problem, pitch manure, program a computer, cook a tasty meal, fight efficiently, die gallantly.*'

Finn. He inspires me. Duende.
And I admire him. I want to be like him, able to cut him out, and off, like he can do with me. What I had

once hated, I now envy.

And as for feelings, I learn to use them for reference, a thermometer, a barometer, not to make too much out of erratic, quickly shifting emotions that change like weather.
This will ease and ameliorate my Female Artist Syndrome.

Conducting an experiment one sunny afternoon, I concentrate all my energy to see if I can read messages from the clouds. After great effort, I experience rainbows like waterfalls cascading from them. In the end, however, the message gleaned is not to waste time on the changeable and fleeting messages of something as ephemeral as a cloud. Instead, focus on the enduring truths beyond them.

Ironic for a screenwriter to give up drama. I am learning to approach art like a firefighter- go into the burning house with flames of emotion, get the word, the scene, image, and then get out before being inundated with the suffocating, asphyxiating smoke of sentimentality.

I enter the flaming building - locate, retrieve and release ghosts.

Briefly breaking from his work, we are talking about future film endeavors. Finn says that filmmaking is a serious sacrifice in which 'someone always dies' – that is, some part of the self is sacrificed in the process of realizing the vision.

'Who died making Red Reign?' I ask.
'I did.' He answers. It breaks my heart to hear this.

Giving myself to life, to art, and to love. Constant perpetual death. Nothing is spared.

Because, he has died for my work, and I die perpetually for loving him, ghosts remain.

CHAPTER TWELVE

illuminable wings

Some ascend, others linger.

He soars to the edge of the atmosphere, near equators and by Earth's poles, occasionally landing in navy satin sheets, a plush robe and ivory claw foot tub. Finn bathes, shaves, has red wine, black tea, a smoke, and then another. But, comfort is taken with caution, only enough to mute sorrows that echo in the deepest darkest wells. Reaching to the core of the earth, its nerve and intelligence centers, where he plugs in and activates.

Soon it is his mother's birthday. She dies of cancer when he is fourteen, an event that sends him traveling the world for four decades.

He gauges me like light in a camera's aperture, how

much can be let in before over exposure. Love with limits. Measured merging.

And, I do the same, regulating the amount of light that I might safely emit.

We, like photographers, control and adjust the light by degrees, F-stops.

F for freedom, friendship, flesh,
fear, filters, fences,
function and form.

But, the results are increasingly beautiful.
Sometimes, even exquisite-
Breathtaking.
Sublime.

The results are sweet moments- exchanges of ideas, eruptions of laughter, an impromptu dance or a foam rubber sword duel, and the art birthed from our connection. Consecration.

So to honor the women who has raised this man, I will make Shepherd's Pie, and vase her favorite flowers, freesias, that grow like gem colored miracles from the moonlike landscape of The Burren, so tells the son.

'That's us.' Finn says, 'We are like the flowers that grow from between the rocks.'

'Like the lotus that grows out of the mud', I add.

Angela is a doctor. Her father and seven siblings are all doctors. But neither their science nor medicine can save her from the brain cancer that will take her life.

We are teenagers when we meet, working at a summer camp. We haven't been in touch over the years, only reconnecting when I find out she is sick. People are more likely to open up and talk when they know you have walked similar grounds. Andrea knew my brother, Jeremy. They would share a cause of death.

She wants to speak, and we do - about brain tumors, life after death, and faith. She has married late in life, her son is only four.

I lie in bed restless. What can I do for her, for her son, what would I do in her situation, leaving behind such a young child?

Would she like me to fly out to New York and film a message for her son?
I imagine what her son would want to know as he grows.

Yes. She wants me to come. She is grateful.

I must move quickly. Her speech is deteriorating.

My salient objective- create something that her four year-old can appreciate now, and as he matures. Something that will comfort him as a child, guide him during turbulent adolescence, as he forms his own identity in young adulthood, or starting a career and family of his own. To remind him that he is loved. Offer insight into his mother as a women, her dreams, her talents and hopes, the ones she had for herself and the ones she has for him.

I will fashion the interview to answer questions that can only come from her, the questions I try to imagine that he will have.

'Play nice.' She says in the video…don't be afraid to be yourself.'

Her triathlete husband is galled, resentful that I am there and that his controlled life is no longer in his control.

I film the view from their East Side NYC apartment balcony, to one day conjure this moment, the moment his mother is still here with him.

I take shots of her books. Her piano, the things that may soon be removed from the home, along with all traces of her.

Like photos of her, once a very beautiful woman. Her eye now droops, she has white cropped short hair, post treatments.

She can't walk. I wheel her to radiation therapy along with the caretaker. Then we go out for lunch, I want to film her at her favorite places, but she needs to sleep most of the time and she doesn't eat much anymore.

This is not the film I had hoped to make, but I must quickly adapt to the present realties, taking advantage of any opportunities of her alert and awake. I grab the camera after her breakfast and we film Angela's message for her son.

"I wish I didn't have to leave you, Zack. But, I'll know how you are doing, I'll be watching you somehow.

You are a beautiful boy and you are going to be a wonderful man. I can't wait to see that. Maybe time will be all switched around, so I won't have to wait, because I don't feel like *I'm* a grown up yet.

I found out you were a boy so I could be prepared for a boy to come into this house, and it has been magic ever since.

I hope you remember to be kind, and generous, think about others. Think about how other girls and boys are feeling, help them to feel better.

Don't be afraid. Speak up. Show people who you are. Don't be afraid.

Do the right thing. Think about what that means to you and to the people around you. You'll know, follow your heart, listen to others, but follow your heart. You know what's best for you, you're good at that.

I want to see you develop a love for books, read, get people to read to you. Love books.

There is so much beauty - friends, family. Make sure they're in your life, it's the most important thing.

You taught me to be strong-willed, to be myself. Thank you, I love you.'

Animated stills of Angela end this video.

During these few days, I am in the presence of grace, where all trivialities have made way for a pristine practice of the essential. She is generosity, ease, bravery, patience, and love extended to everyone in her gaze.

Before I leave, sitting at the dining room table, I ask her if there is anyone else that she wants to leave a message for, I assure her it will remain private.

'Do you want to leave a message for your husband?'

'I think some things are best left unsaid,' says this master of life, as she now masters death. It is a privilege to be with her, sharing and exchanging these precious last days during the winter of that year.

She is gone before her birthday, early spring.

Seasons pass, and my birthday is soon approaching.

At the very same summer camp where I met Angela, I also met Judy. She was the bunk counselor. I was nine. She was my hero.

We correspond after the summer, she writes from college in upstate New York. Her hair is dirty blonde, her stationary is sky blue and her block letter penmanship slants drastically to the left. I keep her letters safely in my musical ballerina mirrored jewelry box, in the top drawer of my white dresser.

I have three dreams of her during this time, in each dream she is dead.

I find out from a friend in the winter that she has drowned in a freak rip tide accident abroad.

In the next dream I have of her, the final one, she is alive.

) ((●)) (

During a massage from my blonde, spiky haired, masseuse friend Patrick, the name 'Abe' comes into my mind.

'That's odd.' I think. 'Why am I thinking about Abe Finkelman, now?' He is a close family friend from the East Coast who has just died.

He must be trying to get a message through to me, I surmise, feeling like Whoopi Goldberg's character in Ghost, when she first encounters a spirit trying to contact her. This, after years of her feigning psychic abilities.

If I think I'm imagining this, which I may very well be, it will surely cut off any possible communication, impeding any way for him to get through.

I try to remain open, straining as if on a poor connection that cuts in and out.

He seems, in my vague, milky perception, happy, free from a sick broken body, light.

'Tell Peggy that I'm am happy.' I seem to hear. And then

something about making her laugh.

I call my mother to explain my awkward position.

She starts screaming. My awkward position increases. 'What are you saying, you spoke to Abe? What are you saying?'

'Well, Mom,' I calmly explain, 'do you remember, years ago, when great grandma came to you in a dream and had a message for you to deliver to your aunts and uncles, telling them to stop feuding?'

'Oh, sure.' She begins to calm.
'Well, it's like that.'

'Oh, ok. Then, you need to call Peggy.'

Like Jonah, and other prophets with difficult messages to deliver, I'd really rather not.

I call her.
'Is this a joke, is this true?' Peggy asks over the phone.
'The truth, the best I know it.'

Now it is *really* awkward.

I've grown comfortable with a level of uncertainty, negotiating my way between worlds, but when others are drawn into this neon gray, my comfort level plummets.

) ((●)) (

Patrick, the spritely blonde, spiky haired, masseuse, dies from aids.

Once, on my birthday, he surprised me with a sumptuous pile of pink rose petals at my doorstep. One of the loveliest gifts I have ever received.

A few days after his passing, while planning a memorial service to be held on the beach, his girlfriend, Tracy, wants me to perform a wedding ceremony for them.

Eee gads. This seems like the worst idea ever. I suspect it will break every universal inter-dimensional law. I pass on officiating their wedding.

They had lived together in a studio next to Davy Jones Liqueur Locker. They had not married.

These are the truths we have to reconcile, accept how life really went, choices we made, or didn't, the tragedies and the miracles that make up a life.

) ((●)) (

A woman I know throws birthday parties every year

for her still born child. This spirit, her child, never even had a *birth* day - and that is the bitterest pill.

At Gold's Gym, Tracy tells me she has met someone new and wonderful. She later marries him in a beautiful outdoor wedding with lots of photos to record the day. Just as well I hadn't married her to her previous deceased boyfriend. She would now have to ask me to officiate the divorce!

Like the one who throws parties for her stillborn child, Tracy's first pregnancy is lost. The infant dies. Eventually she will have a healthy baby girl, move to a small town in the South and make chocolates.

Ghosts and angels mingle, linger, hover, comfort, or haunt.

Renee Monchaty, Pierre Bonnard's one time model, the story transpires, takes her own life in the bathtub, where he often painted her.

Debussy dies of cancer.

Languishing in an insane asylum, Camille writes in 1935 to a friend, 'I live in a world that is so curious, so strange. Of the dream which was my life, this is the nightmare.' She dies October 19, 1943 in Montdevergues, France.

L'wren Scott hangs herself with a black satin scarf on March 17, 2014. She leaves her estate to her long-time lover, Mr. Jagger. He would not marry her but I hear he now has her stuff - nine million dollars worth of her stuff.

When an elderly woman in my first Boston apartment building dies, all her belongings are heaped onto the Commonwealth Avenue curbside. Her life is scattered on pavement.

I consider the contents of my life regularly, per this experience, giving things away to whoever may benefit. A constant sweep of clothes, books, art supplies, pre-empts the day that it is all tossed in the dumpster in the back alley for those to come and pick at, like gulls trailing a fishing boat.

I review the contents, an inventory.
Jeans, leggings. Tops, black, silk. sweaters.
Dresses and skirts. Lingerie.

Footwear: mostly boots, clogs, and clog-boots. Heels.
Coats: A cashmere fur lined Bill Blass from the thrift store acquired during a heat wave, flower embroidered tailored black wool, little black leather jacket with military double sided buttons, grandmother's coco colored fur lined 1940s jacket.
Art supplies: a sturdy easel I inherit from LJ during one of the many times he gives up painting.
Canvas, oils, acrylics, terps, gesso, all forms of notebooks - journals, projects, bits.
Perfume, satin sheets in many colors, hand-me-down comforters.
Furniture: all found in the street or second hand.
Cookery and utencils.
Technology: phone, a working Mac and a pile of PCs that have passed on.
Camera with all sorts of paraphernalia and accouterments.

A cello.

All just stuff.

According to Falun Dafa, one accumulates 'virtue,' a spiritual matter, like credit, redeemable, and 'gong,' an energy born from cultivation practice that can be taken with you after the human skin is shed. But, nothing else, no stuff.

) ((●)) (

I savor and dig into the emotional connection that feeds me and my work, the way the hummingbird sucks nectar from the bottle brush flower, inexorably linked. Life and art, life is art.

The dialogue in my head never stops, though sometimes I wish it would. An ongoing dialogue with Finn continues, as sensory organs record. I experience this world for more than myself. I am a sensory receiver.

Stories are being composed upon my body, that it still responds to, processing beauty, pain, and life itself.

He too, is recorded and imprinted in my body- on and under skin, in nerve endings and nerve beginnings, blood cells, heart ventricles, retina, bipolar neurons, womb.

Imprinted is the screenplay born from these ideas-theories, if you will, musings maybe, asking, in which way we are mutable, influencing and changing each other intellectually, emotionally - and genetically.

The sensory organs take in information from the environment, informing and changing the internal structure of the body accordingly and encoding it.

How might this DNA, which has entered my body,

affect me? Is it possible for his codes to change mine? It would seem surprising if this were not the case.

Epigenetics may hold some answers. But, in the meantime, my imagination will suffice.

Imprinted Log Line:
Can the sperm from a casual sexual encounter alter a woman's genetic codes? After experiencing unexplained feelings and visions, she is led to discover just how much we are biologically coded for, and who and what can change the codes.

Through past and present cell memory from DNA passed down in complex and astounding ways, each one of us is a living repository of all our collective histories, the story of civilization encoded on our bodies in our cells, and each of us, indeed a universe.

At times she believed that she was seeing things for another, like a film camera, like he was somehow part of her system.

IMPRINTED
Tag line: CAUTION You are who you shag.

Genre: sci-fi, fantasy, drama.

'We must not see any person as an abstraction. Instead, we must see in every person a universe with its own secrets, with its own treasures, with its own sources of anguish, and with some measure of triumph.' Elie Wiesel

I jot down notes. Images, as emotions pillage through my system, blistering with input. My body responds to the electrical storm, setting off the sprinkler system. Tears come as I manage the deluge like a lighting rod.

Feel.

Record - input.

Understanding. Ideas.

Create - output.

) ((●)) (

While sitting on the garden patio of the French Patisserie, a middle aged man, unshaven with strong features walks by. He has a camera secured to a thick strap around his neck, across his shoulder.

I have a sudden and clear perception that his face is the result of years of his inner life force, meeting the outer force of life - one's personality or character, pushing outward, as challenges, opportunities, circumstances push and bear down in the opposite direction, creating a mold or imprint of what becomes, one's face.

This is evident in the face of a man I am introduced to briefly but never forget, because he smiles so frequently that lines form around his eyes like sun rays permanently bursting fourth.

'After forty, every man is responsible for his own face,' Said Abraham Lincoln, I believe this is what he must have meant.

phys·i·og·no·my : the art of determining character or personal characteristics from the form or features of the body, especially of the face.

One's essence becomes one's appearance.

Having worked at the flower essence store in Venice, I am aquatinted with many remedies that capture the energetic frequency of minerals, plants and animals. They are ingested in order to balance one's system.

There is a remedy called 'whale' which holds the collective memory. Another, 'otter' represents self-love.

Beech, for those who need to see more good and beauty in all that surrounds them, and Asellus Borealis - nurturing.

I create a spider web flower essence. It aids the ability to create, generate, design, conceive and construct, sourced from within, and then to live at the center, sustained by the creation.

Can one create an essence remedy from a person? Like Jean Baptiste in the book, *Perfume,* I too obsess with essence acquisitions.

) ((●)) (

Today, in a black silk turtleneck and wispy silk dawn blue skirt, I am a wave, flickering in and out. Today I am more out.

) ((●)) (

Sometimes I forget that I also exist as a wave.

'Do you know who you are?' Finn says to me, 'Do you

know how big you are?'
He is sharp.
He wants to cut to the chase, cut to the truth.
He cuts me instead.

His disappointment occasionally leads to contempt for humans, which can surface at eighty proof. Other times, he is delighted to flirt with humanity's offspring. But, in this moment he is frustrated that I seem to fall into the dilution, that I am behaving like the rest of them.

He is right and he is wrong. But, I can't explain to him how this is so. We both flicker in and out of human self and the 'other' self, particle and wave.

Because I drag along this human condition, passed on to me like the shape of my lips and jaw, a predilection to gain weight and learning quirks, all of which bind to me that I might transform them into something whole or holy.

I know too, I am the size of a nebula - living in finite female form with frailty, feelings, foibles.

I used to loathe the transitions -
Rising anxiety with the setting sun,

as day slips away to the other side into darkness.

Now dusk is cherished,
my most comfortable, familiar time,
the deep in-digo, in-between,
minimal liminal,
the gloaming
when I go roaming.

Sorrow and joy forever mingling in a dynamic display of color.

I go roaming
in the gloaming
'cuz my high-light is the twilight,
unless, its midnight in the moonlight,
and you're by my sea side,
holding so tight.

) ((●)) (

My birthday draws near.

I consider how Maude, from 'Harold and Maude', celebrates her 80th birthday. Her last, by design.

Perhaps the solution to the repeating patterns of my life, can only be death- death of the human body or of

human thinking. I rule out the former because this was how I probably got here in the first place, I would only be destined for yet another ground hog day.
Hence...

Midrash 4
I, in a past life, despairing for unfulfilled romance, like Renee Monchaty, and perhaps L'wren, had killed myself over lost love. My punishment or lesson therefore, is to endure the un-kept promise of love, like stillborn children, many times over, learning to respond without despair.

Would I achieve emancipation?

Feeling the pressure of my Karma boring into me, I decide that instead of writing to transmute the pain, I would just sit in the pain under the glow of the super moon. I sit in full lotus meditation. After some time, I sense the tight tangle of scare tissue around my heart loosen, disperse, and dissipate.

Is the spirit's evolution to deeply appreciate life on its own terms - a life of loving all humans, not just directed towards one - a life dedicated to higher principles, selflessly giving with no conditions, perhaps with little or no return. Cebei, a Chinese term for a great compassionate love as only a heavenly being can.

Maybe the curse dissolves over time. Or, maybe I just stop caring that the spell still enshrouds me, maybe I have just given up - something that Buddha encourages. Give it up. Let it go.

Because I am no longer bound by the cause and effect of the particle world. I align amidst potent possibility, riding the wave. The sperm breaking through, initiating life, a chain of processes and growth that lasts a lifetime, and more.

But, sometimes too, that fertilized egg will become a miscarriage, succumbing to gravity. Blood and tissue.

) ((●)) (

I write.

) ((●)) (

How do I do it, rectify all that is shattered? How do I sew that which has been rent?

Spinning straw into gold,
Tribulations into treasures,
Fish eyes into pearls.

If I remember to flicker in and out-
Alchemy and opposites,

chrysalis, from the Greek
Butterfly stroke.
The alchemy of turning,
swimming into gold medals.

The micro and the macro, coiling into each other.

But, this too is missing the point. The very point that my life is pointing me towards- that every experience has led me to - that art, beauty and a divinely directed and dedicated life will bless me, unify, refine and purify me, from which there can be a new pathway, or a ladder out of this world, for them, for those who will come next, the journey and the vehicle.

As long as I remember to let the music pulse through me, letting the electrical storm pass.

Response to aerodynamic, agronomic loneliness:

1. Feeling the depths of solitude, I wonder once again, if perhaps it might be best to simply fabricate a friend to talk to, someone I could write to, express and communicate my inner world so that my existence might not remain a cerebral, internal exercise.

Would I be mad to pursue this tactic?
Would I become mad?
Was this a solution or just a very, very, bad idea?

Suddenly it occurs to me - I do this all the time. My invisible friend is called 'audience.'

2. I, who place great value on intimacy, could feel pained by its void, feeling somehow deprived of an act of revelation, or disclosure of some precious 'thing' to a beloved, who would be enchanted and honored to receive, witness or share it.

I wonder what this thing is that I so desire to share, this small seed or gem, *bigou*, so I go inside my heart to see or hear what is so deeply missing.

All that is there is space. Infinite, cosmic, nebula rich space. I have nothing, that is, no-thing, I am everything.

And all I have to offer another is space, to share this miracle laden vastness with one who also knows that he is a nebula. Where we can create planets or float…

I laugh for three days.

) ((●)) (

Is the ultimate realization that we can change our DNA

with conscious intention? That we are all connected to each other through past and present cell memory from DNA, transmitted by complex and astounding ways, each one of us a living repository of all our collective histories, the story of civilization encoded on our bodies, in our cells, and each of us indeed a universe? We are all composites of each other, carrying our histories. We are all connected.

When I expand myself, that is, recognize my true being, like Lagoon Nebula, there and then, everything comfortably fits - Infinite room for all feelings and experiences, mine and everyone else's, too. Every piece of music, all gesture and every expression becomes the texture and shade of nebula.

But, when in the form of human, woman, Eve to an Adam, flesh and breath, ordered by biology and centripetal force - my experiences, desire, longing, grief, compressed into this form, seem too painful to bear.

I am best when I'm defying gravity, existing beyond the three realms, loving and needing nothing from humanity.

'Whatever the man called a living creature, that was its name.' Says the Bible.

Do names really hold clues to character or destiny as many cultures believe?

Adam named the animals in Eden.

I name imaginary children I won't have. I name films and books I will have. Sometimes they overlap.

After the names of oil paint colors, I conjure a son and daughter Phthalo Blue and his sister, Alizarin Crimson, Aliza for short.
They now live in a musical called 'Open Mike' set in a Venice cafe, a collaboration between me and a local musician.

Reading perfume descriptions evokes imagination. But, *wearing* perfume keeps me from fainting from the fatigue of life exiled from Eden.

Perhaps fragrance is a small reminder of the aromatic combinations of splendor that Eden was. Like orange blossom and violet, spicy anise, carnation and iris and soft vanilla - the ingredients for *Apres l'Ondee*, the perfume of rainstorms.

Like the *havdalah* ceremony, where spices like clove and cinnamon, are used to herald in a sweet week, or as some say, that spices or *besamim*, aid the soul's decent from the elevated state of the Sabbath, into another mundane work week. So, upon the conclusion the of *Shabbat* on Saturday evening, after three stars have been sighted heavenward, a short ceremony with wine, a three wick candle and fragrant spices, is performed to mark the separation of holy from what is not.

Like the *besamim*, fragrance will seduce and rescue me from the despair and ennui of this three dimensional existence. Each trace of scent that rises from my breast revives- comforting, surprising, and encouraging, affirming the act of life itself - breath. In-spire-ation.

Today, bitter almond, caraway, jasmine sambac, moss, jacaranda wood, vanilla and musk bring pleasure to this prickly day. I am wearing Dior's vanilla oriental, *Hypnotic*, with a sheer black frock, over a vintage slip, a dark ruby sweater, suede jacket and boots.

) ((●)) (

Apres l'Ondee, 'after the rain'- I buy to wear on my birthday, and in Southern California, where rain ceases to fall in June, the sky will darken late afternoon of the jubilee birthday, and a lovely shower will burst forth.

I read about perfumes like *Apres l'Ondee,* created by Jacque Guerlain in 1906 while Camille is working on *The Wounded Niobid* sculpture and beginning her descent into darkness. Finn's boat, *Astrid*, is built this same year and will eventually carry him to Los Angeles where we will meet and exchange evanescing, yet enduring gifts. I read about Vintage *Cuir de Russie* by Chanel, inspired by her Russian lover, the Grand Duke Dmitri Pavlovich Romanov, a cousin to the last Tsar, the way some read the Wall Street Journal or mystery novels.

The fragrance notes read like poetry to me, or music, as the language will imply.

Cuir de Russie

Top notes: aldehydes, rose, jasmine and ylang- ylang.

Heart : orange blossom, bergamot, mandarin, sage, iris.

Base: jasmine, rose, ylang-ylang, cedarwood, vetiver, styrax, leather, amber and vanilla.

Ms. Chanel was quoted as saying that this perfume captured the essence of her romance with the Grand Duke.

If I bottle my relationship with Finn, what would be its composition?

Blue poppy, black hemlock, red current and orange blossom - opening, vibrant and intangible.

Heart notes, warm and complex - bulgarian rose, jasminum sambac, datura, honey and immortelle.

Finishing with resonance and depth - vanilla, tolu balsam, jacaranda wood, and musk.

I will call it, *Notre Fil Rouge* or *Corde D'or*
Golden Cords.
Invisible Red Threads.

Or maybe it is a tender and compelling aquatic scent,
evoking both, longing and fulfillment,
the question, and the answer -

Lotus and driftwood.

Freesia, tobacco, peony and plum.

Irish moss, amber, ozone and night blooming cereus.

Lingering.

Perle de la Mer.

Treasures are procured.

So how will this end?

After duality will come consummation.
Ascending to heaven, like Elijah in a chariot made of fire, or mist, or surging waves the color of my eyes.

For years, my sea green eyes remind me of the ocean. Until one day, when peering into the mirror, fire leaps out from the marine like discs, and I know too, by the golden ring around the pupils, that I possess fire.
A ring of fire.

I write.

Shedding layers as I rub words against my skin like Turkish exfoliating bath cloth,

Scattering words like ashes from an urn,
Sloughing off the dead.

On my way home from the cafe, late one night, I tell Finn, 'I found a sand dollar on a beach in San Francisco with a hole in it. I brought you the hole, as a gift.'

We have a belly laugh.

How will this end?

He is planning to leave,
move across the oceans.

Again, I will have freedom.
But, no longer the moments
watching him shave his whiskery face-
The view from the tub,
as I soak in the sweet
salty balm of him.

Free again.
Still the child, escaping from her crib.

I have freedom and these stories, the contents of my life, gathered here in these pages, no longer strewn about the street, and my character, forged by these events and exchanges, and the art it produced in this human world.

) ((●)) (

How will this end?

As incarnation of Queen Macha, the Irish Goddess of birth, death and sovereignty, I will land at the shores of Ireland, dancing to the fiddle, tin whistle, flute and Uilleann pipes, with my brusk and brisk whiskery whiskying man, wearing *Lolita Lempicka,* or *Perle de la Mer,* like the marrow and selkies of the enchanting fishing towns, Killybegs, Kenmare or Dollygore.

How will this end?

I am inclined to declare this my last and final love, that there will be no other man after Finn. As an ending to this book, for the sake of a literary construct, a reflection of my robust romantic sensibility.

Or, perhaps an attempt to deconstruct romantic notions, for either a lack of imagination or faith, or an excess of both, that either he will be the last, or that there will be no other.

If we are not to be together, I will cauterize these memories and feelings, seared with solitude and solace, lest they bleed into nostalgia and yearning - embracing a life chaste, clear, pure, uncompromised and uncompromising.

I am his and he is mine, always, realized now or eventually -

As we will one day be betrothed at the Burren where, carrying a bouquet of freesias, we will wrap ourselves in gold cords for the traditional handfasting ceremony, joined with and to, love and freedom.

Sovereign companions. Autonomous and together.

The zygote, whose union is Life. Creation.

But soon it will be the time to dismantle my treasury of words, and begin weaving them into wings, for these stories will become their intricate design and color.

I buy a new camera, and am off to learn how to use it and then shoot a film. A film to remind myself and other souls in the city of Lost Angels, that hidden beneath the weight of human thoughts and emotions, we are all imprinted for wings-

Volitant, avian, airborne,
skyward, heaven-bound
illuminable wings.

) ((●)) (

This moment, a wave, a sensation takes me, coloring mood and emotion.

I analyze the illusory construct of life, time, the moment, and this moment, acknowledging the way the light casts a golden glow this late winter afternoon. I note the temperature, quality of air, the feelings conjured by the song I'm listening to, combined with the piece that I am writing, the way my clothes feel against my skin, the scent of the perfume I am wearing, angle of my chair, its approximation to direct sunlight, and to Finn physically, as he is sits some yards from me, and to him emotionally, as he reads a book.

And too, the unseen factors at play - proteins, germs and hormones surging in the bloodstream.

I consider where I am in my life within the history, the hour, the time of humanity, the evolution of our species, understanding my place in the cosmos as planets and stars spin and rotate.

Some moments I feel drawn into another realm, forging beyond memories of love and sorrow, lessons and yearnings with golden dust like strands, creating the place where this book lives and is being written. I flicker in and out like an Olympian's butterfly stroke, in and out of air and water, in and out of time and space.

How will this end?

Yearning rolls like seasons
and wheels, towards the human heart,
Spiraling, and recoiling inwards,
and out again,
a certain purr, a hum, a low hungry growl.
It is Rikbiel, overseer of the divine chariot, chief of wheels.
I hover on the serrated edge,
pausing at each ridge to kneel, know it, name it.
I work to set the moon back into the night sky.

And now the next moment.

This is how it ends.

Photo taken:
Killarney Train Station
Kerry, Ireland.

Masha Savitz is a painter, documentary filmmaker and journalist. With a BFA from Boston University, and Masters in Rabbinic Studies, she writes and teaches, while frequenting local cafes and Irish pubs near her home on Venice Beach.

Made in the USA
Las Vegas, NV
28 July 2021